Robert B. Meredith

Noel Noel

Betty Noel
and Christmas

by Robert B. French

CONTENTS

CHRISTMAS
— 1984 —
NOEL BETTY NOEL

BY

ROBERT B. FRENCH, JR.
FORT PAYNE, ALABAMA

DEDICATION

To the True Believers

Other book Robert French has written

The Adventure with John
The LAWyer
Beaten, Battered, & Damned: The Drano Murder Trial
Call Me Herman
Ten For The Road

FOREWORD
FORT PAYNE, ALABAMA

In cleaning out some old files to put in the garbage, I discovered an old manuscript. I had forgotten about it as I had written it during a very stressful time of my life. I had just been required to defend two sensational double murderers at my own expense --- back to back --- and I was broke and sick. I had contracted Graves' Disease and atrial fibrillation due to the stress of the horrible cases.

This true story was written 36 years ago. In re-reading the work, I discovered that, other than Pete and Betty Noel, most of the participants' names were changed.

Apparently, after writing the story, I filed it away without a name. I stumbled across it the second week in January, 2021. The pages were yellowed and crisp. I took it home and read it. What a surprise! I thoroughly enjoyed it and learned from it.

Since I do not believe in accidents, everything happens for a reason, I found it so you can read it. Enjoy.

Bob French
Fort Payne, Alabama
March 2, 2021

IT BEGINS

It was Saturday, the 15th, one of those December days in Dixie only a Southerner knows; one of those warm winter, blue sky, pleasant days that heralds the Christmas Season in the Southland. The Alabama Band sings "Christmas in Dixie," but they add "snowing in the Pines." Rarely does a Southerner know snow.

It was one of those days that Southerners like, warm and blue, with the 1984 Christmas on its way.

It was after lunch. The lawyer was standing in his den, high atop Lookout Mountain, holding a cup of coffee and looking out on his view. The low slung, old brick with a courtyard house was built into the west brow of Lookout Mountain. It was one of the first houses built with the foundation poured into the bluff line. He could see 30-odd miles on that crisp December day. He was enjoying the view that never grew old. He liked the beauty and warmth of the day, sipping the coffee, waiting for the football game to start on T.V.

The phone rang!

As he heard the ringing of the phone, the lawyer winced as if the ringing of the phone was hurting him. In truth, it was, because the ringing of the phone meant that he would have to go somewhere for someone on his only "day off." Ira Williams carefully guarded his Saturdays.

On Sunday he would go to church, take a nap in the afternoon, then devote the rest of the day and evening to his clients. But Saturdays -- Saturdays were his to become one with his thirteen- year-old twins, a boy and a girl, Rhonda and Richard, who were born on the 4th of July. He jealously guarded every hour of every Saturday. Oh, there were Saturdays that he devoted strictly to himself. These were the Saturdays he read philosophy, researched religion, or sat alone on his mountain while his family was off shopping. He watched football games when Alabama was playing. The phone deepened a depression that was already there.

In the week preceding this Saturday, the lawyer had been in Bankruptcy Court pleading his own case. The Court had ruled that he had to pay the sum of $10,000 to a bank within thirty days or lose his office building.

Ira Williams was in bankruptcy because his practice had been forced to fade while he defended two persons accused of double murder within 22 months of each other. He was forced to finance the cases and to defend those appointed clients at his own expense. It was just part of being a lawyer in Alabama.

He often thought about the fact that all the lawyers involved in the Manson Murder Trials were forced into bankruptcy. He had seen his friend from law school, Morris Dees, become the founder of the Southern Poverty Law Center in Montgomery, in order that he might solicit donations to keep the defenses of the defenseless ongoing.

He never realized in the beginning how relentless he would have to pursue the defense of these cases that were costing him money rather than bringing in fees. He lost a total of three airplanes during the 22 months of self-financed trials - a Merlin III, prop-jet, a low time Baron B-55, and a Cessna 310. The planes had to go. The lawyer could not support the aircraft and the cases.

As was his nature, he became obsessed with the defenses of the two double murderers. He despised both clients. However, he was determined to save them from the chair. The first, a man who killed his mother and father, for absolutely no reason whatsoever, was sentenced to life. The second, a girl who kidnapped and killed an orphan, then kicked her body over a 430 foot canyon rim, was sentenced to die in the electric chair by the judge who forced him to take the case. Both cases were sensational news producers that severely hurt his reputation. He had the first case on appeal when he was required to defend the second.

The small town where he lived did not have a public defender. As "their duty to the community," Alabama lawyers were often forced into defending indigent clients. The Court had ordered him to take the two sensational murder cases, *pro bono*, without fee. The girl was his 16th murder defense at his own expense. He knew it had to be politics.

Many of the people in the community hated the lawyer because he did a good job representing his poverty-stricken clients. After the trials had concluded, the lawyer found himself without any business. Old clients did not want to be represented by him. Potential new clients were told by friends and neighbors that the lawyer could not win due to his reputation in the community.

Slowly, he was forced into a financial reorganization that eventually led to Chapter 11 Bankruptcy where he had to pay all his debts on a court's schedule. He was really feeling sorry for himself.

The phone was still ringing.

His thoughts drifted from his view of the skyline to the Christmas season which was coming. He did not have money to give his wife to buy Christmas cards nor presents. He did not have the money to purchase a plane ticket for his oldest daughter to come home from college in Boston. He did not have the money to pay the bills, and he did not have the money to pay bonuses to his office staff. He loved to surprise the staff at Christmas by giving them more money than they thought he would give. He always gave bonuses in time for the staff to shop for Christmas. But this year it was different. The lawyer was broke, worried, and feeling miserably sorry for himself.

THE WILL

He walked to the phone on the wall and put it to his ear. A frantic female voice shouted into the phone, "Mama is dying! She wants her will. She hasn't signed it yet. Maxie and Cynthia are on their way here. Mama is not going to make it through the weekend."

It was Syble Lewis, formerly Syble Noel, on the phone. Her voice was breaking to the point of hysteria. The lawyer could hear the anguish in her voice. And he felt aggravated by it rather than sympathetic.

"She told me last week she was going to live a while longer," he said calmly. Well, she had said it. Betty Noel had told him personally that she was not going to die as soon as people thought. She told him that four days earlier when he visited her to take down the information necessary to draw her will.

"What do you mean she's going to die this weekend?" He queried. "I'm telling you, she told me she was going to live."

He bordered on being adamant. It was apparent to anyone who knew him, he did not have the will typed and ready, and he did not want to give up his Saturday pounding it out on an office typewriter.

"I talked with Dr. Wilburn just a few minutes ago. He said her lungs are filling with fluids. He said he will come in the morning and pump her lungs out and she will die sometime real soon. He could put her on life support systems and keep her alive for a while, but Mama doesn't want that," Syble told the lawyer.

She was matter-of-fact about the situation now. She was giving a report. "Mama said she did not want any machines to keep her alive, and I have promised her that she won't have to worry about them. So, we are not going to take her to the hospital. We are going to honor her wishes and let her die, as she says, 'with dignity at home.' I just hope Maxie and Cynthia make it here before she dies." Syble sounded worried.

"Are you sure she is going to die?" the lawyer asked.

He was trying to avoid telling Syble the will was not ready. Also, he did not want to give up his Saturday if Betty Noel was going to live a few more days.

"Are you sure she is as serious as you think?"

Syble was prone to overreact in a tense situation.

"She's not going to make it, Mr. Williams," Syble stated. "This time she is going to die. . . and she wants her Will. She wants everything in order. Can you bring it by for her signature?"

Oh well, the jig was up. He figured he might as well admit it. "Ah, Syble, I took your mother's word for it. I didn't think she was going to die this soon. So, we haven't typed her will yet. If you are sure Betty is leaving this weekend, I'll go type it. But if you feel she will last until Monday, I will wait and let the girls do it first thing Monday morning."

He was being honest, but trying to wiggle out of typing a will on this beautiful December Saturday in Alabama.

"We need the will. Otherwise, I wouldn't have called you. Mama wants everything in order. I wouldn't have called Maxie in Nevada or Cynthia in West Virginia if she wasn't dying. This is it. We need the will," Syble stated. It was time.

Aha! The lawyer thought of another way to salvage his Saturday. "Well, how is her mind? You know, she has to be fully aware of what is going on. By law, she must know the nature and quality of her bounty, her estate. She must have a lucid interval in order to execute a valid will."

Sometimes he hated himself when he sounded like an attorney. At that moment, he envied the big city lawyers who left their offices at 4:00 P.M. on Friday and returned at 9:00 A.M. on Monday. They were lost on the golf course, or at the ocean, or they were out to eat, or they were at the club when clients like Betty looked for them. Here he was in Podunk, small town U.S.A., and he was on the bull's eye. He had no place to hide. He could only impress upon Syble the necessity that her mother had to have the presence of mind necessary to make a will. Perhaps she had passed that point, the lawyer mused silently.

"Oh, she is totally aware of everything. She knows exactly what's going on. She was the one who told me to call you and have you bring her will over here. This isn't my idea. I'm merely her Executra or Executor or Executary, or whatever you call them, "Syble said, hemming him up.

"Executrix" he corrected her, knowing he had been had. There was nothing left to do other than go to the office and type the will.

"She is going to die then?" he asked one more time.

"She is," Syble stated emphatically. "She really is. This is it. Mama has suffered with that cancer enough. I am not going to take her to the hospital and Dr. Wilburn says this is the last of her life. It's over. The cancer has broken through into her lungs."

"O.K., I'll be there in two hours. Give me time to go to the office and type the will. Tell her to hold on until Maxie and Cynthia get here. That will give me plenty of time to finish the legal work. I'll see you in a few minutes."

He didn't like saying that, but he was committed to it. So there goes another Saturday shot to hell. Christmas is a real Bah Humbug season anyway.

"We'll be waiting for you," Syble ended the conversation cheerily.

Ira hung up the phone and turned to his wife, who was sitting at the breakfast table by the sliding glass doors to the deck, sipping coffee. "Betty Noel is dying" he said, with the full importance of the meaning of the words.

His wife had been a friend of Betty Noel for years. Their children had played and grown up together.

"Oh, no," his wife Annah responded. "I knew she was sick, but not about to die."

"Why couldn't it be me?" the lawyer whined in self-pity. "Why the hell can't I die and get all of this mess over with? You and the kids would have the insurance, you could pay the debts, and I would be out of my misery. Why can't it be me?"

"You don't mean that," Annah said, rising and coming to him at the coat rack where he was slipping into a light jacket. She patted him and hugged him as she had done for thirty years. "You don't mean that, Baby. You are just tired. It has been a long hard week. Now you have to go out again on Saturday. Don't worry about all of these other things. Everything will be alright."

She consoled him to the point of sounding patronizing. However, their relationship was such that her sincerity was known to him.

"Well, it ought to be me. I'm so tired of it. I'm just tired of life. It is really becoming more than I can stand. I'm tired of all the crap involved in living. I just wish it were me instead of Betty Noel."

He was still frowning as he moved toward the front door to get into his '83 Thunderbird and drive to his office.

"Baby," his wife consoled the warrior of a thousand court battles "you are just tired. Go make her will and come on back. I'll have pizza when you get back. We might even decorate the tree today."

She was trying to encourage him as she had done so many times in the past. She remembered when he thought he could not pass an exam in law school, and she remembered when he thought he could not win a certain case, and she remembered when he thought he couldn't close a certain deal. Whenever he thought he was going to fail, Annah always encouraged him. It really didn't matter how she hurt inside, it was the man that counted. It was the warrior, the trial lawyer, the image -- it was the reputation that counted.

"Go on, when you get back I'll have something good." She hugged him and gave him a peck on the lips as he opened his car door to leave. "Hurry back," she urged him.

"O.K., I'll be back in a little while. But I sure do get tired of this life, you know," he said as he started the engine to leave.

The lawyer drove out of his driveway and started south on Scenic Road, high above Fort Payne, Alabama, on Lookout Mountain. He drove a mile or so to Five Points. From there, it was down the mountain, past the courthouse, and on to his office on the street behind the imposing building.

As he drove, the radio was playing "Christmas in Dixie" and Randy Owen, leader of the Alabama band, who lived on Lookout Mountain, was singing in that country whine, "Merry Christmas from Dixie to everyone tonight." Ira Williams didn't see anything merry about it.

Something in the song did seem to soothe the melancholy feelings he was experiencing. After all, the sky was as blue as a bird's egg in the springtime. The weather was pleasant. It was one of those long beautiful winter days when the leaves are off the trees and the sun shines brightly. The lawyer simply couldn't stay in a bad humor or sorrowful mood on a day like that. Furthermore, he was committed. He had to prepare the will and take it to Betty. If she was dying, he might just learn something. "What if?" he thought as he parked his car behind his office building.

He had bought his structure in late 1969. It was an old house built in 1907. Annah had hired Herb Stanley, an architect, and between the two of them, they converted the old house into a sparking law office with boxwoods along the old brick walkway leading to the building entrance. A large pecan tree, growing near the driveway, distinguished it from other law offices in the area.

As he keyed the back door, he wondered if he could come up with the money to save it while he was in bankruptcy. $10,000 in a very few days was going to be hard to raise. It would have been nothing in the old days, but now the murder cases caused his reputation to be tarnished and he did not get the big cases that he once did. He simply didn't know where he might raise the money.

He rummaged around one of the secretarial offices until he found it all: the will paper, the notes in Betty's file, the copy of his wife's will to go by, and an IBM electric typewriter he could operate.

After thirty minutes' typing, the will looked properly professional on old English parchment paper and script. He considered himself an excellent typist.

Less than an hour from Syble's phone call, the lawyer had the will in hand, properly placed in a will binder, inserted in a matching will envelope, and he was on his way out of his office to the home of Betty Noel. She lived less than a mile south of him on Scenic Road.

As he drove, he thought it was ironic that she was named Noel and might die at Christmastime. He knew that she had divorced Ray Womack, the District Attorney, to marry Pete Noel, an expensive ladies' coat and dress salesman from Mississippi. Pete was a recently divorced father when he met Betty. He had four young daughters to raise. Betty had Cynthia by Ray. She had Maxie by Amhitz, an Austrian diplomat in New York. When she married Pete Noel, she became the mother of four additional daughters. Maxie changed his name to Noel. Later, when she divorced Pete, Maxie changed his name again. The lawyer had first met her more than twenty years before when she and Pete were active in politics and civil affairs. She raised Pete's daughters quite respectably. Then he divorced her and left her alone to age and die in a huge rambling brick home.

The large brick and mountain rock house was on the brow of Lookout Mountain. Fenced in, it looked like a foreboding house in a movie.

Syble, Pete's most rebellious child, a middle daughter, seemed to hate Betty while she was growing up, but once grown, her attitude changed. Apparently, Syble realized that her stepmother had given her the social graces, the education, that the environment, and the determination to become an educated lady, career woman, and frustrated actress. Syble was the only stepdaughter to attend Betty after Pete divorced her.

When Betty gave the lawyer the instructions for her will he noted that Syble was the Executrix, and Syble was treated equally with Cynthia and Maxie. He thought it was an amazing statement about Betty and Syble. He had known Syble as a little child. He knew that she had been a hell raiser all of her life.

Syble and her husband, Fred, met the lawyer at the door to the neatly kept imposing, what some would call a "mansion," on Scenic Road.

"Come on in, "Syble invited, opening the door. "She's right in there, in her bedroom," she said gesturing with her right hand.

"Is she conscious? Is she sedated?" the lawyer questioned.

"She has taken a lot of pain medicine, Dilaudid, or something like that," she fumbled for the proper name of the painkiller.

"I thought that was a street drug," the lawyer said as he entered the darkened interior of the home.

"The doctor gave it to her with a prescription. It seems to be working pretty well. I have heard of it before. Do you know what it does?"

"It's a downer."

"Well, whatever it is, it's working. You can go right on in." Syble was leading Fred, two women who had been caring for Betty, and Lula C. Spain, Betty's mother, as well as the lawyer into Betty's room.

Betty's bedroom had been part of a second family room before Betty's illness made her bedfast. Then she didn't want to be off upstairs. She wanted to be near the family. Hence, the lawyer walked through the foyer, living room, adjoining den, and turned left into the temporary bedroom.

"Ira's here, Mother," Syble announced to the half- sleeping woman in the four-poster bed.

Betty turned her head from its side on the pillow to look through glazed eyes at the lawyer.

"Oh, hi, Love," she said clearly, as she recognized her friend of more than 20 years, through the haze of painkilling medication.

"How are you feeling?" he asked.

He noticed a trace of lipstick and eye shadow. Her reddish gray hair was combed, and she was wearing a necklace on her light green silk nightgown. Good ole Betty, he thought. She was always going to look good. She had said it was just being presentable.

"I thought you said last week you were going to live for a while. What happened?" There was genuine concern in the lawyer's voice. He sat in the wheelchair beside the bed. The others stood around the foot of the bed.

"Oh Darling," Betty gestured, waving her right hand out from under the blanket. "I have just become too tired. I wanted to stay around, but it takes too much effort. I'm tired of the pain. I'm tired of being a burden. I'm just tired of keeping on. You know, you come to the point in life where it just isn't worth the effort anymore."

"Yeah, I think I know," the lawyer consoled, remembering his own attitude. "My mother called us all together and told us she was tired of living. My sisters started crying, and I begged her to stay on with us. She finally agreed and hung around for four more months. Then one morning she just decided to die in her chair right after breakfast. Since we knew she was ready and was doing what she wished, we honored her wishes. We had a very pleasant funeral for my mother."

"That's the way I want mine," Betty sighed with a long breath.

It was apparent she was dying. She did not have the will to live, and she was tired of continuing in her life of pain. The lawyer fully realized that Betty Noel would die very shortly.

"She's ready to go," Lula C. reassured the lawyer with a voice having religious overtones.

He was the teacher of a large Bible Class at the First Baptist Church in Fort Payne. Lula C. was a faithful member.

He tried to strike a more cheery note. "Well, here's the will. It's just like you told me you wanted it." He was taking the document out of large white "will" envelope.

"I am so sorry that you had to come out on a Saturday and do this," Betty apologized. "I know how hard you work during the week. I'm really sorry I have to be a burden to you too."

The lawyer heard himself saying apologetically, "Don't be silly. I count it an honor and privilege to serve you, particularly at this time. Can you sign this thing?"

"Well, it's for sure I'm in my right mind. All of them here know that." She looked around the room for assurances.

"That's right" Syble asserted. "She knows exactly what she is doing."

The two heavy ladies, whom the lawyer did not know, nodded fat-faced agreements. One of them said, "Yes, she certainly knows exactly what is happening. There is nothing wrong with Betty's mind."

There was a general clamor of voices in the room agreeing that Betty knew exactly what she was doing.

"Well, let's see if we can sign this thing." The lawyer handed the sick woman a legal pad with the will on it. She reached for the pen with her left hand. His mind raced trying to remember why he had forgotten she was left handed. He could not remember her being left handed before. He kept his mouth shut. He marked it up to age and his memory slipping away.

Betty Noel began trying to scratch her name on the bottom of the legal document. Or, as the lawyer would have said it, "She executed her will at the foot and end of her Last Will and Testament."

Betty apologized over and over for being unable to write plainly. "Ever since I had the stroke I have had to use my left hand to write. I'm just not too good writing with my left hand." She took her time and drew each letter on the paper. Her writing was almost illegible and obviously written with an unsure hand.

Ira and the fat ladies signed the document as the three witnesses. All agreed that Betty was making her will just as she wanted it to be.

After the will was properly witnessed, the lawyer placed the document back into the envelope and handed it to Syble.

"Here you are, Madam Executrix. This is the only copy and it is in your care, custody, and control."

"What do I do with it?" Syble appeared to be ready to hand the document back.

"Just hold it for a while and pass it back to me five days after Betty passes on."

"Well, I'm certainly about to pass on," Betty interjected.

THE DISCUSSION

The lawyer turned his attention back to Betty Noel on the bed. "Are there any questions I might answer about your will, death or whatever?"

He seemed to be fumbling for just the right words. He didn't want to sound too religious. Yet, the words came out that way. He meant the legal ramifications of her estate under the will he had drawn.

"I don't know of anything," Betty smiled weakly. "It is something that is just about to happen. I know that I'm about to die. I really don't want to prolong it any longer than is absolutely necessary. I just hope I can hold on until Cynthia and Maxie get here."

"On second thought, I guess I do wonder about something. If death is so bad, as most people think, why am I looking forward to it? Has the pain overcome my fear?" She asked wanting a serious answer.

The lawyer liked to talk about fear because he believed it motivated so many of mankind's actions.

"All fear can be traced to our fear of death," he instructed.

"Being afraid of death is as natural as your determination to survive. Death is the great unknown. Human beings are naturally afraid of the unknown. However, if we believe any of the great teachers or sages, we realize that really there is no reason to fear death. The reason death is not a fearsome event is the absolute fact that it is going to happen. Every living thing is born to die. No exceptions."

"I know that," Betty said showing interest. "But I have just never been able to understand it the way preachers and church leaders put it down."

"Oh, I know that feeling," the lawyer agreed. "Listen, to really understand death, you must first understand life. Let's look at all creation as if the Atlanta Airport is all the physical reality we know – the world, everything.

Imagine you have a ticket for a flight to take you home to your relatives and friends, whom you haven't seen for a long time. You have missed them since they have been gone and it has been a while. Now, you realize you are going home to join them. You are in the busy airport waiting for your plane's arrival.

"Now, since your plane has not arrived, you are not concerned with boarding the aircraft. It isn't time. You aren't ready to depart for your destination. Therefore, you can only concern yourself with what?" He asked Betty to be sure he had her attention.

"Oh, I suppose you are concerned with waiting for the plane, or actually living," she responded with a weak twist of her head. She was definitely interested.

"That's right," the lawyer stated as though he would tell her to move to the head of the class.

"That's exactly right. The warrior spends his life waiting for his death. You have spent your life waiting for your time to die. Don't you see how it all comes down to these last few hours?"

"That's for sure," the sick woman agreed. "I can see where you are going with your metaphor, but why do people have so many problems during life? Everything is a hassle."

"All of life's problems depend upon how you spend your time awaiting your death. We unravel the events of our lives through our acts while waiting for our departure. Just as we anticipate the event of our plane flying us away to our destination at the end of our time in the airport, so we should anticipate death. Can you see now that we should live ever ready for its arrival?"

"I sure can. When you come down to this point, death is all there is left."

"That's right. Unfortunately, many people spend their entire lives pretending they are in the airport, but their plane is not going to arrive. They race around the terminal buying everything in sight. They buy candy, drinks, souvenirs, and all the other worthless baggage they can find. They stake out the most comfortable place they can find to wait. But they have forgotten they are in the airport to catch their plane. They ignore other passengers or consider themselves better than their fellow travelers. They seem determined to show the world that they can wait differently and more beautifully than anyone else. These passengers represent most of the politicians and wealthy people of the world," he drew a breath.

"Look at how wealth has always caused mankind to place all his efforts in the wait, rather than in the preparation of the arrival of their plane. When their flight is called they aren't ready to leave because the search for worldly goods and services has caused them to forget why they came to the airport in the first place. Instead of the trip, these people are convinced that the airport is all there is. They have become trapped in the time of the wait. They don't even consider going home, even when their flight is called. They are determined to stay in the air-conditioned airport. They are familiar with the noise, the hustle and the bustle, the rush, and the confusion of the terminal. They are only fooling themselves. Their only purpose for being in the airport is their departure for home." He paused before going on.

"Rich passengers seem to run madly around the terminal collecting everything they can find. Some of them cheat, lie, grab, or step on others in an effort to acquire more baggage. When their plane arrives, they discover they can't take a piece of the baggage they accumulated with them. Some say, 'Well, if I can't take it with me, I'm not going.'" He grinned and paused while Betty interrupted.

"Wrong!" She tried weakly to imitate comedians on television. "They're going, but they are leaving all their worldly goods. That's what the baggage is. And you know what? After they catch their plane out of here, people will ask, 'What did he leave,' And you know what the answer is? 'Everything. He left it all. He was only allowed to take out of here what he brought in, himself.' That's, right isn't it?"

She was looking for assurances.

"Right," Ira agreed. "You can see that right now; you are ready for your trip, and what can you take with you?"

"Just me, Darling," she smiled weakly. "I'm going to just take me. That's all I have left now. The will takes care of the rest of it."

The lawyer thought that her realization of that fact was beautiful. He knew it was true.

"I can understand the idea about the rich people. I've seen people like that all of life, but what about criminals? How do they fit in at the airport?" Betty asked.

"Oh, sure," the lawyer replied. "Criminals are very much like the rich people. The desire for wealth is there in both instances, they just go for the money in a different way. The criminals in this world are the passengers in the airport who steal the luggage of the other passengers. They steal someone's seat, they pick someone's pocket, or they trick someone out of money. They persuade themselves that crime offers the only way for them to be comfortable while they wait. Some even commit murder. Just as with the rich, when their flight is called, their ill-gotten gains are going to be left in the terminal for some other foolish passenger to find or fight over.

"I love this illustration," Betty smiled. "The world truly is an airport."

"Well, life is an airport," the lawyer corrected. "Let's carry it a little further. Look at the passengers in this life who are lost in the airport. As with the criminal and the rich, these lost souls, wandering around, never considering the joy of waiting for their plane. They are too busy reading the posters, the advertisements on the walls, listening to the public address announcer, or watching other passengers. These folks explore the vacant corridors of life, or go into the restricted areas. They seem to drift and stray through their lives without ever realizing their purpose for being in the terminal. They are busy entertaining themselves with each new curiosity that they discover, and they never learn to wait. They wander aimlessly until their plane arrives, and they are placed on board by an attendant. These people may mean well in all that they do. They are just too preoccupied with what they are doing to ever realize their death is just waiting to snatch them away. Their plane is on time," he paused.

"If all living is an airport, then why do people fight wars? I guess you know that I'm glad I'm leaving this mess. Any day they may begin the nuclear holocaust which will end the world for all life as we know it. I'm really glad I don't have to worry about that. Why do we have to have an arms race?"

Betty was enjoying the discussion. The airport idea intrigued her.

"Well," the lawyer smiled. "You've seen the gates at the terminals where all the people wait for the same flights? Those areas are the cities. Let me show you how it works."

Betty laughed out loud. The idea of the United States and Russia being passengers waiting at different gates in the Atlanta Airport was funny to her.

"Look at it this way," Ira continued. "Here we have these groups of passengers waiting together in one section of the airport. Other passengers are grouped in their gates in the terminal. Each group of passengers are convinced that they are the only ones who know how to wait properly. They insist that other passengers wait just as they do. They have located some specific place in the terminal which they believe they enjoy more than any other place. They begin to believe that the place they live in is the best place in the airport. They become so convinced of this that they will not allow any other passengers to join them. In religion, these groups believe they are the only ones going home. The others aren't going to the same place because they call their Father by a different name. What we are actually talking about is cities, nations, races and creeds. Do you see it?"

"I do. Keep on," Betty encouraged.

"Well, these groups will actually fight over their geographic position in the terminal or their philosophy of waiting. All wars are fought over how human beings will wait for death. The paradox is that wars simply hasten death for the participants who are trying to change how they, or others, wait for death. I guess this is the cosmic joke. Look at it. Right now, the super powers are threatening to blow up the entire airport if they are not allowed to wait where they wish, or believe in the type of waiting that they wish. To be sure they are doing it right, they constantly spy on the other boarding areas or waiting rooms to watch how everyone else is waiting. They want to know if anyone is imposing their ideas of waiting on them, or if anyone may be considering coming into their boarding area and waiting with them. Groups of passengers, such as nations, are so obsessed with their place in the terminal or their way or method of waiting that they die believing the airport is all there is. History is replete with records of their failures in waiting. Future history will record that we were the silliest waiters of all time. We consider blowing up the entire airport for all time simply because we disagree with others on how to wait." He stopped for a minute because she appeared tired.

"Are you doing okay?" he asked concerned.

"I'm alright," she said weakly. I'm just resting my eyes thinking about Julius Caesar, Alexander the Great, Adolf Hitler, and the like. They didn't know how to wait, did they?"

"Not at all," the lawyer responded. "Tell me one thing any, or all of us, can do to bring one of them back. Immortality is not given in stone or print."

"Human beings have been failures at living, haven't they?" she asked with her eyes closed, a tiny smile playing across her pale face.

"They have been and are now," the lawyer replied. "All of those who have become accustomed to the airport believe their plane will not arrive. Their concourse or boarding area is all there is. Their plane will come for them when they least expect it, and they will leave when it comes. Their gate will be left to the janitors to clean before the next group of travelers arrive. Oh, they cause havoc while they are here, but their departure is hardly noticed. The terminal seems to be a nicer place to wait after they are gone, and they will leave.

"Have you thought of the Peloponnesian War lately, or the battle of Brittan?" He didn't stop to let her answer. The Peloponnesian War was the most ridiculous illustration he could think of. He didn't want to get bogged down in a discussion of Athens and Sparta in the 5th century B.C.

He continued, "The terminal always seems a nicer place when the warmongers are gone. They are hardly ever missed because they spent their time here concerned only with their own comfort or position. Some call it a standard of living or a way of life. And, to the militaristic nation, nothing else matters. These passengers want your pillow to rest on; they want to feel secure; and they want to feel they are better than their fellow passengers. They never consider the aircraft coming for them. They do not concern themselves with their crew, nor their route. It's a pity they board a doomed ship to crash and burn. There's hardly any loss, though.

These folks, entire civilizations of them, were dead when they failed to realize the plane would come and they would not be ready. They were just like so many others, too busy being in charge of a part of the airport, to realize they came to the terminal to leave, not to stake a claim."

He stopped for a minute. He was afraid he was beginning to sound like a lecturer.

He looked at his friend.

She opened her eyes. He noticed some sparkle in them "Oh, please do go on," she encouraged." I like this."

He almost said something to continue, when she interrupted. "Is life as dismal as all this sounds? Where is man's salvation from his own stupidity?" she asked, sincerely concerned.

"Frequently, actually about every 700 years, great spiritual teachers come to the airport and announce the best way to wait for the plane," the lawyer continued.

"The Buddha, Lao Tse, Mohammad, The Christ, are all examples of passengers who told other passengers how to enjoy the time they spend waiting to catch their plane. They always warn the people, 'Don't forget, the plane is coming, be ready to get on board. You're bound for home. It is a happy time. Go to your plane joyfully knowing this was your purpose for coming here. Help others wait, and help the weaker ones board their planes until yours arrives. Share your pillow, your goods, with those passengers less fortunate than you. Treat others as you would have them treat you. You should be happy in the terminal because your Father is waiting for you to reach home, and that is going to be the happiest time you can imagine.' These great teachers instruct us to wait in a manner which will keep us ever vigilant for our plane to arrive. They constantly remind us that we are only in the airport to catch the plane."

"Why don't the people listen? How do they get their words so confused?" Betty was serious.

"Again, you know the answer. The passengers are too caught up in the atmosphere of the airport. Christ said be in the world but not of the world. Most passengers never hear this. They see others leaving on every flight, but do not believe their flight is coming. They will return from seeing someone off and refuse to think about their own departure because of the fear in it. They accept death, but not their own. They believe for an instant that it can't happen to them. If you are in this world you are going to die, life is just that simple." He breathed a deep breath.

"The way of the warrior is anticipating his plane's arrival and waiting for his ship in his own way, and allowing others to wait for their ship in their way," he continued.

"When we realize that everyone has a plane coming to the gate, then we know that waiting is an individual effort. No one can wait for anyone else, just as no one can leave for anyone else. Everyone has a different ticket. Since no one can die for you, why should you allow anyone to try to live for you? All this can do is cause problems."

He continued on, "There is no fear in leaving if you know all along that you are going to leave. Death is the common bond among all people. It doesn't matter what language you speak, what color skin you have, what religious tradition you follow, where you live, nor what you do. You will die. Whether you ever think of it or not, it is appointed once to man to die, and by God, every person will die. Life is only waiting time in the terminal. Look at it this way, if you know all along you are going to die, then there can be no fear in leaving." He looked at her for her approval and understanding of what he was saying.

"Yes, I see that," she said. "But, if all men are going to die, and they are, why do we think this, that and the other is so important? It seems that death is the equalizer. No war is important to the person killed in it after the person is dead. Why do we make things so important? Right now, I can't see that anything in this world is important because I am just about to leave it all. So, what happens on the world news tonight does not faze me one way or the other. I can't even have any feeling about it. Can you explain that?"

She was trying to harmonize her life into categories of important events and unimportant events.

"Because of death, there are no events, or what I like to call acts, any more important that any other event or act." The lawyer began to answer her question.

"People in their folly place great weight on some acts and down play others. This is foolish. The President attending a cabinet meeting is no more important than a woman cooking beans for dinner. The most important act I can think of is going to the restroom when you really have to go. That's important.

"Further, no matter how small, each act may be that person's last act on earth. The last act is the one each passenger performs before boarding the plane. All life comes down to the last act. When that act is performed, it is over. It may be over during the middle of an act.

"When the plane arrives, the airport is gone for the departing passenger. Human beings should perform every act of our lives as if it were our last act on earth. It may very well be just that. Don't you always wave bye and smile your cheeriest smile when you are leaving your friends and relatives at the airport? Death should be the same way." He stopped briefly before continuing on.

"Just as your trip took some pre-planning, so should your death. We did not arrive at the airport without a plan for leaving. We checked the schedules, the routes, the airlines, the price of the tickets, and the time en route. Why do less with life? The warrior pre-plans his life with his departure date in mind. He is always ready when his plane is ready to depart. As this life ebbs away from him, the warrior does his last dance with death. He performs his last acts. He can do this because he has lived in anticipation of this moment. He knew the airport was just a waiting place until his plane came to take him home. He can easily perform his last acts with flair because he has lived his life deliberately." He paused.

"Well, I can see how death is a blessed relief when you are in my condition, or when you are old and feeble. I can see the person approaching death satisfied that it is on its way. But why are we sad at funerals? I don't want any tears at mine," the sick woman was seriously questioning her lawyer.

"Why are people sad at funerals?" He repeated her question. "For the same reason people are sad seeing loved ones off at the airport. We are left behind. We are more alone in our waiting. Our loved one has flown out of here, but we are still left with the unknown of when our plane will arrive to take us away. The person is gone, their waiting is over. Our waiting begins anew with each passing moment when we are left in the terminal. Departure is permanent. Departure is sure. Since it is definitely coming for all of us, we should make it a work of art. It is such a personal thing. Dying is one thing each person must do totally alone. No one can do it for you. So face it bravely, victoriously and confidently. After all, you are a child of the King. You are bound for your Father's mansion. Wouldn't it be nice if the whole world could realize they are just waiting for a plane?"

"Oh, it would be so beautiful if they would," Betty said wistfully. "I love playing with that illustration. It is so simple, so beautiful, and so true. We never did talk about the actual boarding of the plane, the actual dying part."

"Do you know how it is? I mean, do you know what dying really is and how it happens?" the lawyer asked.

"I don't think anyone ever has to learn to do it. After all, everyone is going to do it sometime," Betty replied.

The discussion with Betty had made the lawyer's troubles pale in comparison. He began to realize the futility of worrying about things.

"Well, without going into a lot of religious philosophy, because I know you know all that, do you know about dying itself, the actual physical act? Do you know that it is just a transition, a metamorphosis -- like the change from a caterpillar into a butterfly?"

The lawyer didn't want to sound too forward, but at the same time, he wanted to be sure his client knew how to die. "It's a change, sorta like a ciada shedding its skin and leaving it hanging on the side of a tree. You know what I mean? It's like taking off a tight corset, or jeans you have outgrown. Maybe even a pair of shoes that are too small, but you wore them anyway."

Betty was very interested in the conversation. "Yes, I know what you are talking about. But what about the sting of death? What is that they talk about?"

"Well, the way I see that, it is sort of like a red wash flowing over your entire being. It sorta prickles or stings momentarily as your spirit or soul leaves the body it has been held in all of these years. I think that this is the sting of death, just a red wash coming over you with a light burning or stinging sensation, lasting only momentarily. Now, some people never taste the sting of death. There are some who just seem to make the change and glow with radiant light as they find themselves in the land of the dead. It doesn't seem to matter too much how you move to the other side. The action takes place once you get over there."

The lawyer was lapsing into one of his Sunday School lectures. "It's passing from death unto life, if you can get that concept," he explained.. "It's like a flip, a transition. You don't stop being you. You just throw off that body you have been wearing all of these years. You simply shut down all of the mental processes you have accumulated during this life. You just become you, free of all the friction, air pressure, pain, breath, bodily and mental functions. You are free from all of these things. You become one with your Father -- the Lord."

"I feel very close to God right now," Betty said. "I know that the Lord is waiting for me in that land, like the land of dreams. I have that peace of knowing this. I can see it and feel it so close that I want to go ahead and get this living over with and push on into it. I just can't seem to grasp exactly where it is. Is it in another dimension?"

"Sure," the lawyer assured her. "We are in the time-space dimension of four-square reality. You are about to leave it. You are about to go back where you came from. You are about to remember who you really are. You are going to that spiritual dimension. It is a place of unspeakable joy and happiness. It is a place where time and space does not exist. It is a place where there is no suffering. You know the Buddha said that all life is suffering. As long as you are living, you're suffering. Fortunately, most of us don't realize it."

"How true," Betty agreed. "I know that life is suffering. Right now, it is suffering for me just to keep on breathing and existing. You know, the nearer I get to death the more I realize how much every human being spends just to keep on living. Because we all do this all of the time we don't realize how much of an effort it is to keep our systems goings and to keep the body and mind alive.

I'm telling you, that is hard work. We just don't know it when we are active. I mean, it takes a lot of effort to hold this body together and keep it functioning."

"That's true," the lawyer agreed mystically. "If we listen closely enough within ourselves we can actually hear the sounds of our intensity or our life forces. You can hear the energies which you use to hold this body together. But, you have to listen closely. You have to be as quiet as a seed in the earth to begin to listen to your life sounds. Mystics call it the sound of the universe."

Ira looked around the darkened room. He had been so intently talking to Betty Noel that he had not noticed each person slowly leave the room leaving only him and Betty alone. He was holding Betty's left hand between his hands as he leaned forward in her wheelchair to talk to her.

"I want to be with God," Betty said affirmatively. "I know that I am going to be with God. I just want to hurry up and get there. I'll admit, I am a little concerned about exactly how this thing is going to take place. I guess it is like childbirth when you have never had a baby. You know you are going to have the baby. There is no stopping that. It is just a matter of when and how surprised you are going to be when it is your turn to go through it. I guess that's the way I feel about dying. I want my death to hurry up and get here. I want to have the pleasure of the surprise of seeing how it is when I have actually died. Can you understand that?"

"Sure," the lawyer agreed. "I believe I know exactly how you feel. Just remember, when you get over there, press toward the light. God is light. This is why the ancient Egyptians and others worshiped the sun god Re. Our bodies are children of the sun. The sun sustains life on the planet. It gives warmth, light, and generally provides a Garden of Eden for us to live in while we are in a physical body. When you shed the body, you learn that God is light, similar to the sun. It's just that God is the most beautiful bluish-white light, the warmest and most loving light you can ever imagine. You are about to join God on the other side. You are going to be on the most interesting journey human beings can take. And, you know what's funny? Every person on the planet is going to make that trip sooner or later."

"I know," Betty dragged out the last word. "I know. I'm just so happy that I'm about to get it over with. I am going to wait until Maxie and Cynthia get here. Then I'm turning in my key because I'm checking out of here."

"When you do it, try to do it consciously. You know, like Christ did it. Try to know when you are going to take that last breath. Accomplish exactly, what you want to do before you leave, then go. Go consciously. You know, like Bryant said in his *Thanatopsis*, if I can remember, 'Go not like the quarry slave at midnight, but approach your death Like one who wraps the drapery of his couch about him and lies down to pleasant dreams."

"That is what Carlos Castaneda was talking about when Don Juan told him that the true warrior does his last dance with death. The warrior of this world always knows that his death awaits his next act, right over his left shoulder. Death is always one breath away, always lurking to snatch man away from here. But when you can face death consciously, when you can look death eye to eye, you come away the victor because it is not the end of all things. It is just the beginning of the new adventure. Try to do it with your senses finely tuned and ready. Can you do that?"

"I'll try it," Betty said resolutely.

The lawyer doubted that she would be able to die that deliberately, but he thought it was worth a try.

"I'm going to try to make the transition wide awake. They had better not dope me up to the point I don't know what's happening. And, they certainly better not keep those machines on me to keep my heart beating. I have told the children all about this. Now, I want to die in peace. I told Dr. Wilburn that he better not put me in the hospital and keep me alive with some pump operating off of electricity. If they ever put you on that thing, they won't pull the plug. You know that, don't you?"

"Yeah, I know that. I'm with you. I don't want that crap either. I want to make my exit about like a shuffle off to Buffalo," the lawyer joked.

"I can see that dance," Betty smiled.

She noticed that she and the lawyer were all alone. "We've seen a lot of it, haven't we?"

"I guess we have seen our share," the lawyer responded. "Don't you think it's funny how it all goes around?"

"Sure, and then it comes around," Betty was smiling weakly.

"Listen, if you are tired, I'm getting out of here," the lawyer rose to leave.

"Oh, no, it's not that. I'm tired, but I'm enjoying talking to you. It's these drugs. They make me groggy at times. Don't leave now." Betty groaned; the pain was more than the pills could stop.

"Are you hurting bad?" the lawyer asked. He was definitely concerned.

"Yeah, I'm hurting bad. I've been hurting bad for a long time. I'm ready to stop hurting. I don't want to drown from the fluid in my lungs. I just want this thing to go ahead and do away with me. It sure has been a long time in coming. I am more than ready for it to end."

It was obvious Betty wanted death to terminate her suffering.

"When Maxie comes, he will help me die a little more. But you said I could ask you something else if I wanted to," her voice trailed off. She wanted assurances the lawyer would answer her next question.

"Anything, just ask it. You know that I'm a strange man. You have always known that I'm a strange man," he smiled assuring her.

"Yeah, I know that. You have always been a little weird, but then people always said I was somewhat strange also. What I want to know is: if I really go out like this, will I ever have to come back?" She was very serious.

"No way. If you really know that there is something else, if you know the Father has another place for his children, then you don't ever have to worry. This is what Jesus was all about. This is what all the great teachers have always said. All you have to know is that you are going home, and you're off the wheel."

"Oh, thank God. I was worried about that wheel," Betty said resignedly.

The lawyer wondered if she knew what the wheel was. He had heard of it in the Hindu tradition, the cycle of conception, birth, growth, maturity, decline, death, conception, birth, etc.

Yet, she seemed to know about it. He was not convinced of it because he did not want to admit to accepting reincarnation as a fact. Still, more and more, he saw in the words of Christ or the Buddha, or some of the great prophets or sages, reincarnation as a fact until the human being knows something better than the ignoble pursuit of worldly goods -- money. He believed that it is the acceptance of the knowing that there is something else that takes the person off of the wheel the lawyer thought. But still, he just wasn't sure. He was sure that not believing in something else is the unforgivable sin.

He responded quickly, "No, you don't have to worry about the wheel. You are off that forever. You know the difference. You have passed living 101. You never have to take this course again. Once you know there is something else and once you decide you want that something else, that's it. You don't have to mess with this place anymore."

"Okay, that sounds good," Betty said with a hacking, painful cough. The lawyer knew she could not last much longer.

"I think you understand it," he said sincerely. "You are going to make it. When do you think you will throw off this life and go on?"

"Well, I don't know. Maybe tomorrow after Maxie and Cynthia get here. Otherwise, I may do it on Monday. We'll see." she sounded very tired.

"I know you are tired. I'm leaving," he was kind.

"I guess you had better. I must save some of my energy in order to wait for Cynthia and Maxie. I don't need too much of it, but I need more than I'm using up right now." She obliviously needed to sleep, and she needed another pain pill. With sleep and a pill, she might last a while longer.

The lawyer stood up, "Look Baby, I'm gone. I'll keep up with your progress. If you need help from me, let me know. Remember I love you, always have," he was standing near the bed still holding her hand.

"I know that, Darling. We have been close, even when we were far away. I won't be like Houdini and come back to haunt you. **I'm** going, and I am going to stay gone. But, when you are ready to come on over, I'll be waiting for you, just on the other side," she smiled a weak, sickly smile, yet one with joy and satisfaction in it.

"Bye, Baby," the lawyer let go of her hand and walked into the music room of the home. Everyone who had left the bedroom had gathered in the music room. This was a corner room with windows around the two outside walls.

"She'll be okay," the lawyer assured the family. "I know she is going to be okay."

"Oh, we know she will be all right," her mother, Lula C., stated unequivocally.

"Yes, she's okay," Syble agreed with her. "Just as soon as Maxie and Cynthia get here, she'll go on. She's ready."

After goodbyes all around, Ira left. He returned to his home in a reflective mood, a strange reflective mood that assured him that the passing of Betty Noel was important.

The lawyer flipped on the large T.V. screen in his game room. The sports announcer was saying that the two teams were playing the most important game of the season. When the world news came on the commentator said that the hi-jacked plane with American hostages in Iran was the most important news story of the evening. The lawyer felt that the football game did not matter. The kidnapped Americans did not matter. The only thing that mattered that Saturday was that Betty Noel was dying. He watched "Solid Gold," and the number one song in America did not matter to him. The only thing that mattered was that a human being was leaving here.

Ira heard nothing further from the family so he slept through the night. In Sunday School the following day he asked each of the women seated on either side of him if they had a report on Betty Noel. Each showed painful shock and said they had heard of no change in her condition.

One said, "She has serious cancer, you know. Poor Lula C.."

Betty had not died on Saturday, nor did she die on Sunday.

THE OPERA HOUSE

During the church service, the lawyer's wife Annah told him, "You know they are having that thing at the Opera House this afternoon?"

She was talking about the high school band concert honoring the five authors in Fort Payne. Annah knew the lawyer would not want to attend because he considered Sunday afternoon his resting time. Since the twins were in the band, he had no choice but to attend the concert.

"Okay, we'll go," he whispered. "I think it's at 2:00."

"Good," Annah whispered back relieved. "I'll tell the children you will be there."

The Fort Payne Opera House, an old building constructed shortly after the Civil War in 1889, had been neglected and was in gross disrepair. By 1965, it had been stripped, gutted, and totaled as a theatre, where once Lillian Gish had performed. The lobby had been converted into an upholstery shop.

Its three-story-high tin roof leaked in at least two dozen places. Miss LaWanda Culver, an old maid, had inherited the property from an aunt of hers. In 1965 she wanted to sell it for $60,000.00. Although she dreamed of someone purchasing the building and restoring it to a theatre, she was willing to sell the property to any legitimate purchaser.

In 1967, seventeen years earlier, Ira and Charles, his partner, came to an agreement to dissolve their partnership. The disagreement was over sharing the new office building that they had built near the courthouse.

Since the building was on land owned by Geneva, Charles's wife, Ira had no choice but to find another place to practice law. He found a strange little building, 30 X 30, across the street from the decaying Opera House. The tiny building did have a basement and the lawyer converted that into his law library. He practiced there temporarily until he could find a permanent office nearer the courthouse.

While counseling Betty Noel regarding her possible divorce from her husband Pete Noel, the lawyer told her he was considering buying the old building across the street, converting a portion of it into a law office, and use the rest for the benefit of the city as a municipal auditorium. "Those old theatres are hard to find these days."

Betty was immediately interested and suggested that they restore the building into what it once was -- a Vaudeville theatre. She and the lawyer talked about the restoration project on several other occasions.

One day, on the pretext of having some furniture recovered, they walked through the darkened interior of the old theatre past the upholstery shop. They were amazed at how beautiful the building once was and could be again.

Ira contacted the new owner of the building, Paul Hawkins. He offered to sell the building to Ira for exactly what he had paid for it, $60,000. After Ira raised the money, he told him that the roof leaked in at least a dozen places and would cost $30,000 to replace. Ira realized the purchase and restoration of the old building was out of the question. $90,000 was a lot of money in 1968.

He and Betty Noel entered into a conspiracy to save the old building. Although Ira was Chairman of the Ft. Payne Arts Council, they agreed that the two of them were not important enough to bring about the old building's restoration. But, if they could get Lula C. interested, she could plant the seed with some important townspeople and the building might be restored.

Betty's mother was all for restoring the old building. She had fond memories of great performances there when she was a girl during the early '30s. She talked with several influential women around town, who had also attended performances in the old building, and had great memories. They were all in after she had convinced them that it was their idea to restore the building.

They organized a Landmarks Corporation with the sole purpose of "Saving the Opera House." They recruited influential men (mainly their husbands and their friends), politicians, professional people, and the general public.

The lawyer had moved from the Board of Directors of the Chamber of Commerce to the Tourist Association, and from there to the Chairmanship of the Arts Council. He immediately began an anonymous publicity barrage highlighting the city's need for a concert hall and civic center.

To make a long story short, the community supported the restoration of the Opera House for more than three years. When it was completed, it became a national landmark. It was a beautiful old brick three-story structure with the original marquee.

On the Sunday of the band concert, as Betty Noel lay dying, the Fort Payne Opera House was in mint condition. It had been completely restored to a magnificent antique theatre, where the price of a ticket would buy two hours out of the past.

The lawyer and Annah sat in slick old wooden contoured theatre seats under the balcony. He looked for Rhonda and Richard. He spotted Rhonda in the saxophone section on the stage, but he could not locate his son in the trumpets. He concentrated his attention on the band students on the old opera house stage as the old theatre was beginning to fill. The third-floor balcony had been roped off. The main floor was almost packed. The townspeople were crowding into the old building. All the Judges, lawyers, the textile mill owners, the doctors and their wives, businessmen, professional women, ministers, teachers, the works. Everyone who was anyone was there.

Ira looked around the darkened old theatre while the high school band fidgeted on the stage. It was ten minutes before the concert was to begin. He spotted his son in the trumpet section. The lawyer smiled at the painted walls, with the murals of the history of the area painted in beautiful colors, he looked at the beautiful old lights hanging from the high vaulted ceiling, and he enjoyed looking at the gorgeous green curtain Betty Noel had swiped out of the Loew's Temple Theatre in Birmingham when urban renewal restored downtown Birmingham.

Betty single-handedly robbed the old Loew's Theatre building of all the necessary theatrical furnishings and fixtures required to restore the Opera House in Fort Payne. The renewal people were happy to get rid of the interior of the

Loews. She had to struggle to raise the money for the trucks to haul the stuff that she had staked out with the contractor's approval. The lawyer remembered giving her $100.00 on the trucking bill some 14 years before the band concert honoring the five authors.

He thought about the parts Betty took in the Fort Payne Little Theatre when the community theatrical group was formed. He had always secretly wanted to take a part in a play, but people said he was too much of an actor in Court. So, he couldn't afford to play a part. The lawyer remembered the giant tassel that hung on his dining room wall at home. He saw similar giant gold tassels hanging from the rich old velvet curtains Betty had taken from Loew's Temple Theather.

When the Opera House was almost completely restored, Betty took the lawyer off at a party one night and said conspiratorially, "Shall we drink to our overwhelming success, Dahling?"

Only the two of them knew the full meaning of her words. They were alone on a balcony overlooking Little River at Billy Jones' cabin at Alpine. Jones owned all of the legitimate theatres in Fort Payne.

"You have performed magnificently, my dear," Ira lifted his wine glass in a salute. Betty, a good-looking, vivacious red head, in a strapless green velvet evening dress responded with a raised glass and a secret smile.

"We did it, didn't we, Dahling?"

The lawyer thought she sounded a bit like Tallulah Bankhead.

"You did it, my lady," he responded. I just nudged it when you wanted it nudged."

Both of them knew that the lawyer had used his position with the Arts Council like a tool to effectuate what Betty was doing through the dowager town ladies. It had been a beautiful conspiracy. They had worked secretly time and again to push the project through. Wealthy women, with purple hair and brittle nails, wondered why Lula C.'s daughter Betty, was so interested in the Opera House. They could understand the President of the Arts Council being dedicated to the project.

"I'm sending you something, Dahling. We may sell them as a fund raiser later, but for now, I'm sending you a tassel from the old Loew's Temple Theather curtain. Do whatever you wish with it. I may give it to Annah if I see her first. Anyway, whatever you do with it, it is my gift to you and our commemorative plaque that we put the bit together and made it work. I'll keep a tassel just like it," Betty's eyes twinkled over the rim of her wine glass in the moonlight.

The lawyer liked his tassel. He remembered that Betty may have sold it to Annah for $100 to raise money for the Opera House, but it didn't matter. The representation of the tassel was what counted. He always thought of Betty when he looked at the tassels.

He would always secretly laugh knowing that he and she had pulled one off on everybody in Fort Payne, and had built a monument to prove it. It was even sweeter that no one was in on the secret other than the two of them. Annah knew that the two of them had a great interest in restoring the Opera House, but she had no idea how dedicated they were to the project.

As Ira breathed the musty air of the old theatre, he noticed that almost every seat was filled. The building would hold 431 people. It appeared that at least 400 people were in there for the concert. He remembered when he sponsored the Chattanooga Symphony to raise money for the building program. Only half as many showed up. The closest thing to this crowd was the Star-Spangled Singers, a group organized by the town, in 1976. They were so good they were invited to perform at Independence Hall in Philadelphia on July 4, 1976. The Star Spangled Singers had almost filled the Opera House, but not quite. Now five authors, their relatives and friends, and the mothers and fathers of 137 band members, packed out the Opera House.

The lawyer thought it was appropriate that the Opera House be packed to capacity while Betty Noel lay dying.

He controlled an impulsive urge to run down the aisle, mount the stage, and yell to the people gathered, "Hey, everybody. Hey, you people in fur coats! Betty Noel is dying right now. You are here in memory of her. Don't you realize this is her warrior's last dance with death? Don't you know this is her swan song? What would she ask for out of this life other than to fill this old building with people? You know she worked for this place. She suffered to see it finished. Yet, none of you know that it was her idea to save this old building from destruction. She thought of it! Betty Noel made it what it is today, and she lays dying. And we are all part of her warrior's last dance with death. Betty Noel has conquered death. She has drained the last perfection from her life. Filling this hall today is her greatest dance!"

Truly he wanted to shout those words, but he didn't. To be as brave as he was, he certainly was a wimp sometimes.

The concert was uneventful. The lawyer found his mind wandering constantly back to the bedside of his friend Betty Noel. When the concert was over he pretended to be waiting for his children while he walked around the old Opera House one more time.

He went through the roped off doors up to the main balcony. From there he went up the winding stairs to the third balcony. He was all alone as the high school bandsmen were packing up their instruments on the stage. The house was almost empty.

He leaned on the bannister and looked out over the near vacant building, "Rest well, Betty, rest well. I enjoyed being a part of your monument."

Betty's experience facing death had given the lawyer new hope for Christmas. He was actually beginning to feel good. He wished he could solve some of his financial problems. He checked her home after the concert. "No change."

FINANCES

On Monday morning the lawyer's secretary told him at 9:00 A.M., "We are overdrawn at the bank."

He winced in anguish, "How can we be overdrawn at the bank?"

The secretary began to enumerate the checks he had ordered written.

'I just can't be overdrawn," he whined. "I keep up with it too closely."

"Well, you are," his secretary reported. I have just brought the bank book down and the balance is over drawn when you count that automatic insurance check that comes out of the account every month."

"What insurance check?" the lawyer asked incredulously.

"The one that comes out every month. I have been here eight years and it has come out every month since I've been here. It is an automatic withdrawal, some kind of life insurance policy you have had for years. You have just for-gotten it. It's $66.50 a month."

The lawyer began to go over his account books and found that his secretary had neglected to include the $750.00 fee he brought in on Friday afternoon. As he was breathing a sigh of relief and placing the bank book back into its proper drawer, Bart Burton, the insurance man, conveniently walked into the office. Burton was interested in selling the lawyer's secretary a cancer policy.

The lawyer recognized his voice and came out of his private office to ask Burton about the monthly draft. Burton was not familiar with the draft as he had only been serving as the lawyer's agent for some ten years. He made some calls to his home office and discovered that the draft had been taken from the lawyer's bank account for more than nineteen years – a little over $15,000.

It was an ordinary life, Key Man, insurance policy that the lawyer had bought when he was partners with Charles lawyer back in 1965. When the partnership dissolved Charles had allowed his policy to lapse. Ira T. Williams had kept his policy in full force and effect. Each month the premium was withdrawn from his firm's bank account.

Burton, balding and a little paunchy, followed the lawyer down the hall to his private office. He was carrying his leather insurance man's brown bag down the hall with him.

"Look Ira," he whispered, so he thought that the secretary could not hear. "I don't want to meddle in your business, but that policy has some pretty good cash or loan value if you need the money."

"I need money desperately!" The lawyer assured him. "I need it bad for Christmas and to save this office building. What have we got to do to get it?" He was anxious.

Burton took the lawyer's policy and began to calculate the loan value. "It looks like to me you can borrow $21,500.00 on it. Now, that will decrease that amount when Annah gets it if you die, and you don't pay it back. You understand that, don't you? The cash-out value is somewhat less. But I wouldn't cash it out. Take some or all of the loan value, if you gotta have it."

Burton was chewing the stump of a cigar that had never been lit.

"I'm not interested in the world **when** I'm dead," the lawyer pointed out. "How quick can I get the money?"

He was secretly counting the days left to buy his oldest daughter's plane ticket from Boston, and the number of shopping days left until Christmas, so that Annah would have time to buy presents for the twins. Then, there was always that order for the $10,000 payment within a few days.

Burton fumbled through his insurance man's leather bag "Ha! I thought I would have a form here. Just sign here please, and you can have your money as soon as it can be processed through the office."

"Mr. Burton," the lawyer said appreciatively. "I do believe you are Santa Claus."

"Well, maybe one of the elves," Burton laughed. "No, I'm too big to be an elf. I must be one of Santa's helpers."

Burton continued laughing as the lawyer signed the form. The insurance man checked the form, folded it, chewed on the cigar stump, and started walking out of the office.

"Ho, Ho, Ho," he mimicked Santa Claus as he went down the hall through the waiting room and out the front door.

The lawyer's secretary bounded into his office. "I can't believe it!" she squealed excitedly. "We've got money! And not a minute too soon. I heard him tell you we might have it by Friday. What do you think?"

"I think we'll have it," the lawyer assured her. "Since we know we'll have it by Friday, I guess you might as well go ahead and write all the necessary checks. Give Annah $700.00 for Christmas, buy airline tickets at the travel agency and have them delivered to Marsha in Boston. Then we will talk about Christmas bonuses." He winked at his secretary.

"I'm writing already, and I'm ready for the bonus. I guess you know this is not a minute too soon. I was afraid we would not be able to buy much Christmas this year. It's been a rough time. But, I guess we have a real genuine Christmas miracle, don't we?" She was joyous.

"We sure do," he assured her. "We sure do." The lawyer was smiling contentedly, leaning back in his large office chair.

Ira opined, "Other than Christmas, the best part is I can comply with the Order of that Bankruptcy Judge. I had just a few more days to raise that $10,000 and I had no idea how to do it. What a relief."

If a person could have listened very closely, the lawyer could have been heard to say, "Thank you, Lord." From that time on, Ira T. Williams, Attorney at Law, felt good.

MOVING ON

It was almost noon when the lawyer called Betty Noel to see how she was progressing with her dying.

Cynthia answered the phone. "Oh, Mr. Williams, this is Cynthia. Thank you for calling. Mother said how much your last meeting meant to her. Thanks for talking to Mother. She really enjoyed it. She told us some of the things you guys talked about. Maxie and I really appreciate it."

"It was my pleasure," the lawyer responded. "How's your mother?"

"Well, there hasn't been any improvement. I guess she will go any time. She has had Maxie in there for most of the morning. I think they have been talking about the kind of things you and Mother talked about. So I just don't know. Someone will call you when she passes."

"Thanks," the lawyer assured the young woman he had known since she was a small child. "Please let me hear how she comes out."

Early Tuesday morning, before 8:15 A.M., the lawyer answered his phone. Syble said excitedly, "Mother died last night around 10:30 P.M. It was great. She called us all to her bedside. She remembered a lot of the funny things and the good times we had growing up. She laughed more than she has laughed since she has been sick. She was telling Cynthia and Maxie about how they were born and joking with them about how they were right after they came into this world. She told all of us how much she loved us. She told us she was leaving for a better place and for us not to worry about her. She was alright. Then, she smiled so sweetly and turned her head on the pillow and died. We were all there. It was such a beautiful experience. The family just wants to thank you for making it a little easier for her."

"That's good," the lawyer was sincere. "That's so nice. I am happy for you and Betty. When is the funeral?"

We aren't going to have a funeral. Mother said she wanted to be cremated. We should have the ashes back here by Wednesday.

We'll have a little private memorial service then, or we may not.

We just don't know what we are going to do. Maxie and Cynthia are staying here in town until the ashes come back from Birmingham. I'll let you know what happens."

The lawyer was impressed. He had often thought how nice it would be to be cremated rather than go through the funeral, the cemetery and the burial routine. The thought passed through his mind that one day the entire earth was going to be cremated anyway, when the sun begins to swell and fade. Why not cremate bodies? Certainly, there is nothing to be gained by cemeteries and burials. He admired Betty all the more for being cremated. He wished he could do the same.

On Wednesday, Syble came to the lawyer's office. She was literally beaming. "Well, we have just had the best time. The three of us took Mama's ashes and went along the brow of Lookout Mountain and threw them off into the wind. It was so nice. She would have loved that."

"I'm sure she did," the lawyer responded. He came around his desk and hugged Syble. "I hope you have a very Merry Christmas."

She said, "I'm having the best Christmas of my life. This Christmas I received the greatest gift I could ever receive. We are told all the time about how to live. Everyone you come in contact with knows what is best for you. There is always someone standing around you who will tell you how to live."

She was smiling from ear to ear with joy, "But this Christmas, I received the gift of how to die. Mother died much the way she lived, like a beautiful work of art. I hope I can go half as beautifully as she did. It was so good. It showed me that I have nothing to fear from death. Once you realize that, then you know that you have nothing to fear from life. After all, it's only being in time, isn't it?"

"You've got that right," the lawyer responded. "It has been a beautiful Christmas for me, also. I thought it was going to be a real 'Bah Humbug' season, but Betty Noel changed all of that. Merry Christmas!"

"Merry Christmas," Syble beamed. "I love you. It is so much easier to say that to everyone now. I guess because I mean it. Isn't it easy? Merry Christmas!" She said as she went down the hall and out of the door of the office and into the season.

The lawyer leaned back in his chair and looked at the ceiling of his office for a long time. He reflected on the things he had learned during the Christmas season.

"Christmas is not just about living, but it is about dying as well. The baby, whose birthday is celebrated at Christmas, was born to die, as all babies are. The baby born at Christmas taught man more about dying than human beings care to realize.

'Betty Noel,' what a name for a person who died at Christmastime. Betty Noel -- Merry Christmas Betty, rest in peace."

THE REAL STORY OF CHRISTMAS

BY

SAINT LUKE

Provided by Bob French
Hope You Like History

FOREWORD

The primary authorities for facts surrounding the First Christmas are Matthew and Luke, writers in the New Testament. Of these two, Luke is the most reliable. Therefore, in expanding and explaining my research into the original Christmas -- birth of Jesus -- I will rely primarily on the Gospel of Luke together with other historical records.

The writings of Luke were either discovered in the latter part of the first century, or early during the second century. It is thought that Clement mentioned the book as early as A.D.95. It is known that Theophilus of Antioch lived during the second century. It is unknown whether he is the Theophilus mentioned in the first few lines of Luke. The gospel is mentioned as the work of Luke by the Muratorian Canon, based on a fragment found in A.D. 170. This document is the earliest list of New Testament books ever located. Iraneus said that the gospel attributed to Luke was genuine in A.D. 180. Clement of Alexandria, Tertullian, Origen and other early scholars agreed.

Most scholars think that Luke, or "Loukas" in Greek, was a Gentile. He has a Roman name. However, many Jews often adopted Roman names. For example, Saul of Tarsus was the Roman Paul.

One thing is certain, Luke was a very well-educated man. His book is written in the classic Greek of the day. The other Gospels are not written with the ability of the writer of Luke. Among religious scholars, this fact increased their suspicions that Luke was a Greek. Obviously, he had an excellent Greek education. A Greek education during that day and age was equivalent to the best education money can buy today.

The opinions of early scholars and the other evidence almost proves conclusively that the Gospel of Luke and the Book of Acts were written by the same person named Luke. In the Acts of the Apostles, Luke wrote of events taking place shortly after Jesus was crucified. He also wrote of events 30 years later when he wrote about his adventures with the Apostle Paul. We know that Luke was accompanying Paul when they tried to get passage to Macedonia. Luke describes Paul's vision of the man asking him to come over to Macedonia. Then, he writes about their attempt to follow up on the vision. In Acts 16:10, Luke says that, "And after he had seen the vision, we immediately endeavored to go into Macedonia, confidently inferring that God had called us to proclaim the glad tidings of the Gospel to them."

The Book of Colossians was written by the Apostle Paul during his first imprisonment in Rome in A.D. 62. In Colossians 4:14, Paul says, "Luke, the beloved physician, and Demas, greet you." We know that Luke was with him then. This phrase has caused many scholars to believe that Luke was a Greek educated medical doctor who was Paul's personal companion and physician. In Second Timothy 4:10-11, the writer says, "...Demas has forsaken me, having loved the present world... Only Luke is with me..." The importance of this statement is questionable as the author of Timothy was probably not Paul. Also, in the letter to Philemon Paul mentions Luke as one of those sending greetings.

The argument for Luke being a Gentile from Antioch is supported by the details of the city he discussed in Acts. Many of the Christians in Antioch were retired Roman soldiers or retired government workers. Roman pensions were important to the area's economy. It was the Roman capital of Syria. The Jewish community was relatively small among the people in Antioch. During the third century, Eusebius, in writing an early church history, said that Luke was a Syrian living in Antioch.

Scholars have problems with this thesis because Acts 13:1 says that there was a Lucius of Cyrene in the Antioch Church. Were there two of Lukes, one from Syria and one from Cyrene? Lucas was a common Latin name. If the writer of Luke was Lucius of Cyrene, then he was probably a Jew.

Cyrene had a very large Jewish community. The city had been founded by Battus in 603 B.C. The Greeks built Cyrene to be the Athens of Africa. It was a Libyan city in North Africa, west of Egypt, located some 2,894 feet above the Mediterranean Sea. Due to its elevation and the sea breezes, the city enjoyed a fantastic climate. It was an oasis in the desert attracting commercial interests and travelers. It was the home of several distinguished scholars. The Egyptians annexed the city in 231 B.C. Cyrene was later willed to the Romans by the last Ptolemy.

The Old Testament does not mention Cyrene. It is important in the New Testament because at the time of Jesus, wealthy Cyrene citizens had built their own synagogue and quarters in Jerusalem. It was sort of like owning your own motel at your destination. They were coming to Jerusalem to worship at the temple. Their synagogue provided quarters for them. We can imagine that the living quarters stayed filled all year long. Simon the Cyrene was required by the Roman execution detail to carry the cross of Jesus. This act immortalized the city in history by Christian evangelists.

Luke writes his book in the sophisticated tradition of Hellenistic historians. When he lapses into the vernacular, he does so with polish and flair. He is an accurate historian writing some of the most powerful descriptive writings in the New Testament. His knowledge of Medicine and seafaring are apparent from his books.

One interesting aspect about Luke is his relationship with Mary the mother of Christ. It is obvious he was close to her. He may have spent time with her while Paul was in prison at Caesarea.

All conjecture, writings and traditions would be in harmony if Luke was a citizen of Antioch who had grown up and was educated in Macedonia. He was very familiar with Philippi. This is a strong indication Luke was a Macedonian. He probably studied medicine at the Greek school of medicine at Philippi, and spent many years in Macedonia.

He was a very likeable person. He was very interested, very caring, giving, always wise and reserved. He was called beloved because he was an all-around great guy. He was a good researcher, an aggressive scholar, and a person whose loyalty was unquestionable. His father was probably a freedman of some Roman family. How Luke was converted to Christianity is unknown. Probably he was a proselyte who was very familiar with the Greek Old Testament and believed Jesus was the Messiah.

He accompanied Paul on his second missionary journey. He joined Paul at Troas. It seems he remained at Philippi until Paul had finished his third missionary journey. Then he re-joined Paul at Troas and went with him to Jerusalem. He accompanied Paul from Caesarea to Rome. They were shipwrecked together. He stayed with Paul while he was under arrest. Luke actually stayed with Paul until the end when the apostle was martyred. Somehow, he was spared. Earlier, Luke had been described as the brother who was famous among all the churches for his preaching of the gospel in II Cor. 8:18. Taken together, Luke's books are the history of the first church. The Gospel of Luke has been received without question as authentic.

Irenaeus of Lyons, who lived from A.D. 130 until A.D. 202, was born in Asia Minor. When he was a boy, he was a pupil of Polycarp who was born in A.D 30. In his letter to Florinus, Irenaeus said that every time Polycarp taught, he told about how he had known John and others who had known the Lord. Irenaeus discussed the gospels. He said that Matthew wrote a gospel to the Jews in their own language. Mark wrote the sermons of Peter, and Luke the companion of Paul, put down in his book the Gospel preached by Paul. Then afterwards John wrote a Gospel at Ephesus. Irenaeus then quotes Luke at length in his writings.

The actual date the Book of Luke was written is uncertain but the facts indicate a close approximation. The book was written before A.D. 70 when Jerusalem was destroyed. After the third missionary journey, while Paul was imprisoned in Caesarea for two years, Luke was in Palestine. This was A.D. 58 and 59. This period would have given Luke plenty of time to research the evidence and record and complete his gospel. The nativity- narrative indicates that Luke actually talked with Mary about her experiences. He writes about psalms and experiences that only Mary would know about at the time of Luke. He spent his time collecting material from people who knew Jesus. Due to his educational training he wrote as accurately as possible the words and experiences he was told by eye witnesses.

Most of the evidence indicates Luke was never married, and died in Bithynia when he was 84 years of age. A bare tradition holds that he was martyred in Greece. Another holds that he was nailed to an Olive Tree in Gaul, or France, when he was 80 years old. Another holds that he and his wife were crucified together.

CHAPTER ONE

WELCOME TO THE ROMAN EMPIRE

During the time Luke was becoming a Christian, aiding the Apostle Paul, and writing his gospel, the Roman government was in its usual turmoil since the death of Augustus. The emperor was Claudius and he could not control his wife, Messalina. He knew that she was unfaithful, but he would do nothing to curtail her sexual appetite. She disguised herself and with her friends prostituted herself in the sleaziest parts of Rome. Finally, she engaged in a filthy public sexual relationship with a handsome young senator, Gaius Silius. This affair was so well known, so filthy, and so outrageous, it was considered treason against the state.

It was widely believed that Silius and Messalina intended to seize the throne for themselves as representatives of Claudius' son, Britannicus. Still, as was his nature, Claudius would not act. His freedman, Narcissus, acting entirely on his own ordered both Silius and Messalina killed. They killed Silius, but Messalina insisted on killing herself. The praetorian guard observed her suicide to be sure she was successful.

In A.D. 49, Claudius Married his niece Agrippina, the daughter of Germanicus, and sister of Caligula. This incestuous relationship was a scandal throughout the empire. The Senate gave the emperor a special dispensation to continue in the marriage. Unlike Messalina, who was more interested in sexual adventures, Agrippina was more interested in raw political power. Claudius was 59 years of age. He was too tired of intrigue and betrayal to stop his wife. During the final five years of his reign, Claudius withdrew from the public.

Agrippina took over. In public she was arrogant. In private she was chaste unless a political advantage was to be gained. Then, she could be as much a slut as Messalina had been. She was driven by the need to acquire more wealth. She considered wealth a necessary evil on the way to power. Agrippina took Rome into a near dictatorship. She commanded complete obedience from everyone coming into her sphere of influence.

Agrippina knew that Claudius would not live long. She persuaded the emperor to adopt her 12 year old son from her marriage to Lucius Domitius Ahenobarbus. Upon his adoption, the child's name was changed to Nero Claudius Drusus Germanicus. Nero immediately challenged Claudius' son, Britannicus, as next in line for the throne.

To prepare Nero to rule, Agrippina persuaded Claudius to recall from exile in Corsica, the celebrated stoic philosopher, writer, orator, and intimate of her sister, Lucius Annaeus Seneca.

Seneca was perhaps the most brilliant man of his time. He was delighted to return home. He enjoyed the challenge of returning home to tutor the future emperor. He knew that Nero would succeed Claudius because Agrippina was a woman without scruples and would stop at nothing to insure that her son was emperor. Seneca also knew that his pupil came from the most disturbing genealogy in Roman history. He was a mixture of the promiscuity of Julia, the bestiality of Postumus, and the madness of Caligula. His father had serious emotional problems and substantial character flaws. When Nero was born, Domitius Ahenobarbus told his friends that any child born of himself and Agrippina could not help but have a detestable nature and would be a public danger. Ahenobarbus died of dropsy three years after Nero was born. Agrippina was quickly exiled by Caligula and Nero was left in the care of relatives, a barber and a dancer. Seneca knew that his job was to mold the erratic Nero into a model of Stoic conscience and duty. It would not be easy, and we know now that Seneca would not succeed.

Agrippina would not allow Seneca to teach Nero philosophy because she considered it a waste of time. Seneca used diplomacy as an excuse to teach Nero moral and ethical stoic principles. Between A.D. 49 and A.D. 54, Seneca taught Nero eloquence and morality. He polished Nero's character as much as the boy's nature would allow.

In October, A.D. 54, Claudius died suddenly after eating mushrooms. Palace gossips said that he had been poisoned by Agrippina. If she did kill her husband, she had selected the best time to do it. Nero was beginning to attract attention and Britannicus was on the verge of challenging him. With Claudius alive, Britannicus would have succeeded his father as emperor. With Claudius dead, Agrippina could force Nero in as his successor.

The Senate was glad to be rid of Claudius. He had spies everywhere. He was extremely two-faced. He had developed an administrative council staffed by loyal, overly zealous freedmen, who were considered particularly obnoxious to the Senate. They did not hesitate to name Nero emperor.

He was 17 years old when he became the most powerful man on earth. Seneca wrote all his speeches and made most of his administrative decisions. This made him appear to be much more intelligent and efficient than he actually was. Nero promised to clean up government and return Rome to the golden age of Augustus. He said that he would rule by law rather than imperial order and he would respect the rights and duties of the Senate. To the praetorian guard Nero donated a bonus similar to the generous bonus awarded to them by Claudius when Claudius succeeded Caligula. He pledged lower taxes to the people and awarded cash to the plebes. He refused the title to emperor and would not allow gold or silver statues to be made of him. He refused to allow the Senate to rename the month of December after him. They wanted to change the calendar to begin the first of the year with his birthday within the month of December. Everything Nero did or said pleased the Senate. It should have, the acts and words were Seneca's.

Nero's reign was heralded as a new age for Rome. However, Nero had a darker side. He had suffered through a horrible childhood. He had been exposed to ugly sexual orgies as a child and now, as he approached 20 years of age, he began to show traits of mental illness. He was a paranoid, he was constantly fearful, and he did not subscribe to any moral standard. He was the classic sociopath, a man without a conscious. He desperately wanted out of the control of his mother, but he was deathly afraid of her. There were constant rumors in Rome that Nero was committing incest with his mother. He was trying to move his mother aside. In less than a year, Agrippina was out of the power loop.

In retaliation, Agrippina told Nero that she was going to give her support to Britannicus. Nero lacked the courage to murder his mother. But, at a banquet that winter, Nero directed the murder of Britannicus. In a blinding rainstorm the following morning, the body of Britannicus was buried in an unmarked grave. The Senate pretended nothing had happened. The murder was excused as a matter of state.

Seneca wrote a paper describing acceptable political behavior. In it he said that the Roman imperial system required a dictator. He claimed that Nero had been chosen from among men to do the work of the gods on earth. To do this job, Nero had been given the power of life and death over all nations. He could determine the condition and control the destinies of every race and every individual on the planet. This was an absolute prerogative. Nero had the duty to use his power for the people. The people were to remain loyal to the emperor so long as he treated the people with compassion and respect. Seneca failed to realize that Nero had entirely too many emotional problems to be vested with this power and responsibility.

A little more than two years after taking office, at age 19, Nero became thoroughly bored with governing and turned the government over to Seneca and Burrus. Nero began to handle important things such as building a new wooden amphitheater which opened with games that featured four hundred bears, three hundred lions, and gladiators who did not fight to the death. The Senate had forbidden the death of gladiators in the arenas of Rome. This did not last long. The people wanted the fights to the death and the Senate finally allowed it.

About the time of opening the arena, general Corbulo was dispatched to evict a Parthian puppet from the Armenian throne, and the campaign in Britain began to extend the Roman frontier beyond Wales.

Nero imported the greatest lyre player in the empire to give him lessons. He also began to develop his voice. He would lie on his back with a slab of lead on his chest, use enemas and emetics to keep down his weight, and he would not eat foods considered bad for the vocal chords. He made his public debut in Naples. After he finished singing the theater collapsed. This did not stop Nero.

Nero was quite a sight on stage. As young as he was, he was very heavy with a very large bay window and skinny legs. He had a bloated neck, small black eyes, and feminine features. He looked like a person who was always afraid. Usually he appeared before crowds in flowing, flowered robes, slippers and a scarf.

Nero said he wanted to be a musician, but secretly he wanted to be a chariot driver. In A.D. 56, he practiced racing secretly for weeks. Finally, he went to the races at the Circus and raced with professional drivers.

He had married Octavia, the daughter of Claudius, but he was obsessed with a freedwoman, Claudia Acte. Seneca attempted to stop this affair by encouraging Nero to go into the city in disguise at night with his friends and get into all sorts of mischief. The disguised noblemen went into the worst parts of the city and visited the roughest taverns looking for fun. They rolled drunks, robbed bar patrons, broke into shops, stole merchandise, and smothered drunks and threw them into the river. One night the incognito Nero attacked the wife of a senator. The husband beat Nero severely. After that, Burrus, who ran the emperor's household, a praetorian perfect, would not allow Nero to go into town without an armed escort.

In A.D. 58, Nero took back over governmental affairs intending to glorify himself as the world's greatest actor. In A.D. 59, at age 23, he became infatuated with Poppea Sabina, the wife of one of his drinking and carousing buddies. She was a beautiful woman who was a mystic devoted eastern cults, particularly Judaism. It was she who persuaded him to murder his mother. Nero arranged for Agrippina's boat to sink as she crossed the Bay of Naples. The boat broke apart and sank as planned, but Agrippina found a piece of wood from the ship, and using it as a float, she swam ashore.

While the emperor was waiting to hear of the untimely death of his mother, she sent a message to him to rejoice as she had survived the sinking ship. The emperor fainted when he heard the news. He decided that the praetorian guard would kill Agrippina. Burrus, the perfect of the praetorian guard, would not allow the place guards to murder the daughter of the great general Germanicus. This would have been an insult to Rome. A freedman named Anicetus, went to Agrippina's room with several regular army officers and killed Agrippina with a sword. Nero told the public that his mother had committed suicide after she had tried to kill him and had failed. The Senate publicly expressed relief that the emperor had been saved from his mother's plot. Agrippina was cremated the night of her murder, but her ghost pursued Nero the rest of his life.

It was during this day and age that Luke worked on writing his gospel. He had the Gospels of Matthew and Mark to study. He had the oral traditions and his research to facilitate the work. He had listened to Peter, Mark, Barnabus, Paul, and many other eye witnesses of the life of Christ.

Luke wanted his book to be the most complete information available about the life of Jesus.

When Luke was finished with the story of Jesus, he became a reporter by keeping a diary of the events taking place in the Book of Acts.

CHAPTER TWO

THE COMING OF JOHN THE BAPTIST

The preface of the Book of Luke is clear, concise, and a model of Greek introductions of that day. It is written in the purest Greek of the Gospel, and the work is written in the most polished Greek of all the New Testament writings. Great classical writers like Thucydides and Livy were familiar with preparing opening sentences for their important works, and they did so with great literary flair. Luke was very modest and briefly outlined his diligent investigation into the facts surrounding Jesus Christ. He mentions the care he has taken in his thorough investigation, his slow arrangement of the facts, and his authority for writing the book and his purpose in doing the work.

Luke pointed out that many people had attempted to draft a narrative of the facts which Christianity is based upon. Luke felt a responsibility to try to put down all the known information about the birth and life of Jesus once and for all. He was not implying that the other people writing about Jesus were incorrect or unsatisfactory. He simply said that another narrative about Jesus was needed.

Whether Matthew and Mark were written before Luke, we do not know. We believe that they were. We know that the Gospel of John had not been written at the time Luke was writing. Scholars today believe that Luke had both Matthew and Mark as source materials when he wrote his book.

It is probable that at the time Luke began to assimilate his Gospel, there were many writings purporting to tell various portions of the life of Jesus. Perhaps some had been passed around and eventually lost. Apparently, many of the narratives about Jesus had not been accepted as genuine. These writings could have included the apocryphal gospels we know today. Books like the Gospel of Thomas, Nicodemus, and others were written after Luke.

Luke mentions that his work is based upon the oral traditions from the eye witnesses as well as the other narratives which were available at that time. When he said he that he had received information about Jesus from eye witnesses, he used a Greek naval term to describe these people. He called them under-rowers, or sailors who served. In other words, he received much of his information about Jesus from people who had actually served Christ and others.

Before he began to write, he traced all the facts from their original source. He said he went back to the first. This would certainly mean spending time with Mary the mother of Jesus. The Greek words that he uses here indicate that he was practically part of the facts he was exploring. He was sifting the facts as if he were side by side with them. In other words, to write his gospel, he used the most diligent care in investigating the facts. He indicated he was inspired from above to exhibit great dedication toward this work. He was going to use what he had that was good and he was going to work into those accounts the results of his research. He was not necessarily going to write in chronological order, but he would group his facts, events and teachings in a clear order as to inform and teach the reader.

Luke addressed his Gospel to Theophilus. This was a very common name of the day meaning, "Friend of God." This indicates the book could have been written to the Christian community, or it could have meant a specific person named Theophilus. Some think Theophilus was a Roman governmental official who had expressed an interest in Jesus. Others say he was a nobleman in Antioch. It is interesting that Luke dedicated the Book of Acts to Theophilus as well. The title, "Most Excellent," indicates that Theophilus was an individual.

Luke says that his purpose in writing is that Theophilus might know with certainty that the things he had been taught about Jesus and Christianity were true. This book would be a carefully written narrative about everything known at the time about Jesus Christ.

Luke said that his story began with a Jewish Priest named Zacharias. His saying that indicates that it was probably during the spring of 4 B.C., the thirty-third year of the reign of Herod the Great, when Zacharias, an elderly Jewish Rabbi, took his turn to serve a week at the temple in Jerusalem. He was a good man and his wife was a good woman. They were both descendants of Aaron which made them members of the Tribe of Levi. Due to their heredity and status, they were probably Sadducees.

When Zacharias arrived in the Holy City the narrow streets were packed with peddlers, pilgrims, and passersby going about their business in a hurried manner. There were foreign languages being spoken in every nook and cranny. People were crowded into Jerusalem from all over the world.

Although he had traveled to Jerusalem several times before, Zacharias would have joined other pilgrims who were approaching the temple for the first time.

He would have been overwhelmed by the sight of the magnificent building. The Temple would have appeared to be brilliant flame as the sun reflected off its golden dome. He would have fallen on his knees with the others, and thanked God for the beautiful temple. He would have smelled incense, burning meat, animals, dung, and the strong smell of sheep and goats. Beggars would have been aggravating everyone they could in an effort to get money. The city would have been dusty, noisy, and crowded.

Zacharias' destination was the temple complex that covered almost 35 acres on Mount Moriah where it was believed Abraham offered up Isaac. The complex consisted of a series of ascending court yards. The outermost court yard was the Court of the Gentiles. A warning was written on its walls that no one other than a Jew could go further into the temple on pain of death. Fourteen semicircular steps led up to the next court, the Court of the Women. This is where children were presented to God. This is where the purification rights were performed by the women. This was the last court yard the women could enter. The next ascending court yard was the Court of Israel, or the Court of Men. This court yard contained fifty-foot-high columns. When Jewish men stood between the columns, they could see through the eastern gate and watch the priests in the Court of the Priests perform their duties of offering sacrifice to God and generally worshipping Yahweh. Beyond the Court of the Priests was an innermost court yard with a single altar of uncut stone. This was supposed to be the very rock where Abraham prepared to offer his son, Isaac as a sacrifice to God. Within this place was the Holy Place which housed another altar, the table with the shewbread and the menorah. Behind this area was the Holy of Holies, the home of God. This site was so sacred that the High Priest could only enter the area once a year, on the Day of Atonement, or Yom Kippur.

All Jews were bound by duty to visit Jerusalem and sacrifice and pray in the temple at least three times a year.

The first temple had been built by Solomon. This temple had been destroyed by the Babylonians in 587 B.C. The second temple had been built by the returning Israelites returning from Exile. Zerubbabel built this temple. It was destroyed sometime around 63 B.C. Herod then built the third temple which was larger and more ornate than either of the predecessors. The near completion of the temple was a great triumph for Herod shortly before Jesus was born.

Herod was an Idumaean, a descendant of Esau. As such he was distrusted and disliked by the Jews. Herod was determined to modernize Palestine and make it part of the Mediterranean community. He hoped the construction of the temple would help his sagging popularity. It did to a degree. Wealthy Jews formed a political party, the Herodians, which devoted itself to aiding the king. All Jews recognized that Herod had helped Israel and had built a beautiful nation.

The temple was not the only building project of Herod. He had built a palace in Jerusalem, a theater, and an elevated road across the city. He built a luxurious palace in Jericho, and many fortresses which he used as prisons when necessary. He built one entire city and named it after his patron, Augustus Caesar. He named the city Caesarea Maritima. To show his loyalty to Rome, he also built a temple to the divine emperor Augustus.

Although Herod was the King of Judea, the Jews were overshadowed by a much larger Gentile population. His kingdom was a patchwork of communities of Jews, Greeks, and other nationalities. The northern portion of the kingdom was almost completely Gentile. All the groups interchanging with each other on a daily basis created some serious hatreds. Herod, the master politician, balanced their conflicting interests for a very long period of time. Herod also knew that his kingdom was important to Rome as a possible military buffer between Egypt and Syria. Additionally, Herod's kingdom stood between serious Roman interests and Parthia, a kingdom of the Mesopotamian warriors who had fought with Rome off and on for 200 years. Rome had worked to keep the peace with Judea for more than 100 years. However, when the Jews caused problems in 63 B.C., Roman General Pompey crushed the resistance in Jerusalem and brought the area under Roman domination.

Pompey appointed Hyrcanus to be the high-priestly ruler of an ethnarchy consisting of Galilee, Samaria, Judea and Perea. Antipater, an Idumean, was Hyrcanus' senior officer or vizier. Later, Antipater persuaded Hyrcanus to appoint his oldest son, Phasael, perfect of Jerusalem, and Herod, his second son, governor of Galilee. Julius Caesar was assassinated in 44 B.C., Antipater was murdered in 43 B.C., and Hyrcanus was carried off by the Parthians in 40 B.C. Herod escaped and fought the Parthians until he could escape to Rome. There he persuaded Marc Antony and Octavian to support him in suppressing the Parthians and ruling Palestine. 13 years from the assassination of Julius Caesar. Octavian emerged as the victorious Augustus and defeated Antony at Actium in 31 B.C. It was a time of confusion and Herod acted to consolidate his kingdom. He defeated the Parthians in a series of skirmishes, suppressed the Maccabees or the Hasmoean dynasty, and in 30 B.C. was confirmed by Augustus as King. He never wavered in his support of the emperor throughout his life.

Herod enjoyed great independence due to the fact Augustus believed in allowing people to do their jobs. However, he never allowed Herod the luxury of forgetting that he was the boss.

Herod managed to be the friend of Rome while never offending the Jews. He did make a mistake when he hung a golden spread eagle above the temple gate to the Court of the Gentiles known as Herod's gate. Although similar eagles were featured in Jewish history, in their art, and in their religious tradition, they took offense to Herod, an Idumean, putting a golden eagle up on the gate of the temple. They said it was a graven image and their religion forbade worshiping any graven image.

In March, 4 B.C. the huge gilded eagle flew atop the gate to the Court of the Gentiles to the disgust of the Pharisees. The Pharisees were a religious political party called the "Separate Ones." The Pharisees believed in their day somewhat like Baptists believe today. They saw the entire creation as God's Temple, each person was a High Priest responsible for his or her individual salvation, and the individual was completely responsible for his or her closeness with God. This is the priesthood of the believers. To accomplish their goals, they tried to reform the Jewish religion into strict religious observances and formal ceremonies. They dedicated their lives to the Law. They lived to keep the written Law and the oral interpretations of the Law. Although they claimed to be the separate ones, they rigorously attempted to sway the rest of Jewish society to their vision. They lived every moment of their lives attempting to be one with God by, "getting it right." The Law was the measure which allowed them to know whether they were doing it right and whether others were doing it right as well. They learned by observing the piety of themselves as compared to the piety of others.

The Pharisees constantly derided the temple priests and their rival Jewish party, the Sadducees. These were the descendants of Zadok, David's High Priest. They dominated the temple and the commerce there. They also dominated the government. They believed in a practical interpretation of the Jewish Religion rather than individual ethics. They got along with Herod and more importantly, they worked diligently to get along with the Romans. The Pharisees despised this compromise with the devil. They had a saying that they repeated, "We cry out against you, O Sadducees, for you declare pure a channel of water which flows from a burial ground."

The Pharisees were middle class people, who lived very simply among the population, rather than in fine homes. Their attention was almost completely directed toward God. They were the scholars. They insisted that others become educated as well. They ran schools in every synagogue and every Jewish boy had to attend.

The reason there were people called Teachers of the Law was because there were Pharisees who had studied to the point they had knowledge which should be shared with others. Such Pharisees knew that it was their duty to teach others the way of salvation which was the way of the Law. They believed that when Israel turned away from its sins, and reunited in the service of God, the oppressors would be vanquished from the land and Israel would be free again.

The Teachers of the Law taught in local synagogues, in the home of a student, in a court yard, on the hill sides, on the shores of the lake, or near the river. They taught the resurrection of the dead, and the three "R's", repentance, resistance, and redemption. At the time, the most famous Teachers of the Law were Shammai and Hillel, each of whom had a school in Jerusalem. They always challenged each other on points of Law. Herod despised them and attempted to stamp them out. This made them more popular among the people.

Mattathias ben Margalit and Judah ben Zippori, Teachers of the Law, who had their own following, told a gathering of their disciples that Herod's blasphemous eagle must come down even if they had to die to do it. They preached the benefits of dying for God, their entry into the eternal life, and the everlasting joy awaiting each of them. Although it was said the teachers whipped the students into a frenzy, in actual fact, they would never have touched the eagle had they not believed that Herod's death was imminent and he was too weak to do anything about what they were going to do.

A group of about 40 students carried ropes, axes, and other tools as they pushed their way through the crowds in the streets of Jerusalem. Two leading disciples climbed to the top of the arch of the gate. They used ropes to let themselves down to where the eagle was hanging and cut it down. The crowd looking on was shocked as the other disciples smashed the golden eagle into small pieces beneath the gate. Many people in the crowd immediately ran away, but the teachers and their disciples waited. They were arrested and taken before Herod.

Herod had ignored similar incidents in this past, but now he was dying of cancer. He couldn't get out of bed. He had ten wives and sixteen sons. In 7 B.C. he had executed two of his sons for plotting the seize his throne. Previously, he had killed their mother for the same reason. Augustus thought that he was very funny when he said it would be better to be Herod's pig than Herod's son. An Idumean would not kill nor eat a pig, but Herod would kill his own sons.

There were many intrigues surrounding the dying king. He was having recurring bad dreams, or strong hallucinations, where two boys were standing over his prone body swinging a sword. Then, just before the incident with the eagle at the temple, Herod received word through his spies that his son Antipater, who was named after his father, was planning to poison him. Herod was feeling terrible, his life's work was falling apart before his eyes, and he was in no mood to be bothered. Coincidentally, he was aware that there was a wave of nationalistic sentiment rising among the Jews. They were openly hostile to Rome whenever possible. They were preaching that a Messiah would arrive any day and liberate the faithful and elevate the Jews to be rulers of the world. These hopes were spreading rapidly, primarily through the Pharisees. Herod thought that these rabble rousers had to be taught a lesson.

When the Teachers of the Law and their students were taken before Herod, he wanted to know if they were the vandals who had destroyed his eagle. They admitted that they were, and then they lectured the king on how wrong he was to have put the eagle up on the temple in the first place. They told the king that they were bound by the Laws of God, and the Laws of Moses, rather than his rules. Herod considered this statement outright publicly admitted treason. He pronounced them guilty. However, he was too smart to punish them in

Jerusalem. He knew that he might incite a riot. Augustus did not appreciate hearing about riots. Herod ordered the Jews taken by military escort to Jericho.

Jerusalem is 2,710 feet above sea level, Jericho is 800 feet below sea level. The teachers and students walked the 23 miles downhill to Jericho while Herod was carried on an enclosed stretcher. When they arrived at the town the Jews called, "the deepest hole on earth, Jericho," Herod left the Jews under guard in an amphitheater. He promptly convened the leading citizens of Jericho and the surrounding area. Lying on a stretcher, coughing and spitting up blood, Herod did not accuse the Jews of destroying his eagle, instead, he accused them of ingratitude. He pointed out all the great things he had done for the Jews and the thanks he got was the destruction of his eagle. As he recounted the good he had done for the people, he made the audience admit that he was right. Yet, for all the good he had given the people, these Pharisees had insolently trampled upon his goodwill and abused his handiwork in broad open daylight. They had pretended that they destroyed the eagle to embarrass him, but they were really temple destroyers guilty of a sacrilege against the most Holy God. The witnesses agreed that the people deserved death, but they begged that only their leaders be killed. Reluctantly Herod agreed. He was smart to the end.

On March 13th., Mattathias, Judah, and the disciples who had pulled the eagle down were burned alive. Herod then made sure the other students were handed over to other authorities for secret executions. Herod died less than one month after the Jews were executed. He barely had time to order the death of his son, Antipater, for attempting to poison him. He actually died five days after Antipater was executed and buried in the dungeon at the fortress Hyrcania, named after Herod's original patron.

It was into this world that Zacharias, the Sadducee, was ordered to serve in the Temple for one week. It would be the experience of his life time because he would come face to face with a supernatural being, he would be given a sign, and eventually a son. His son would be John the Baptist.

Four of Herod's children are mentioned in the New Testament: Archelaus, Herod Antipas, Philip, and Herod Philip. His grandson Herod Agrippa I, and his great-grandson Herod Agrippa II are named by Luke in the Acts. Herod the Great had a flourishing and even brilliant reign. He rebuilt the nation to where its living standard was near equal to the rest of the world at the time. He was a smart, shrewd, cruel man who did great things while being guilty of great atrocities. He cursed his son Antipater before he had him killed and buried in an unmarked spot in the dungeon of Hyrcania without benefit of final rites nor prayers. He wanted his son to have no hope of an afterlife.

Zacharias had a common Jewish name meaning, "remembered by Jehovah." He was a member of the Abijah division of priests. In 1 Chronicles 24:10 Abijah was the name of the eighth course of the 24 courses David divided the priests of the families of Eleazar and Ithamar into. Only 4 of the 24 courses returned from the Babylonian exile. Each of the returning courses numbered around 1,000 members. From these four courses, the original 24 were reorganized. The 24 courses rotated through the temple. Each course served six days and the Sabbath. Their duties consisted primarily of taking the offerings, preparing and offering the sacrifices, offering the incense, and generally serving God and the worshipers.

Elizabeth was the wife of Zacharias. Her name means, "vowed to God." She was from a priestly family, probably the tribe of Judah. She had married into a priestly family, possibly the family of Zadoc. Priests were allowed to marry under certain conditions. See the authority for a priest to marry in Leviticus 21:10-15:

> "He that is the High Priest among his brothers, anointed with the special anointing oil and wearing the special garments, shall not let the hair of his head hang loose in mourning, nor tear his clothes; he shall not be in the presence of any dead body, not even his father's or his mother's; neither shall he leave the sanctuary when he is on duty, nor profane the sanctuary of his God: **I AM THE LORD.** And he shall take a wife in her virginity. A widow, or one divorced, or a woman who has been defiled, or a harlot, these he shall not marry; but he shall take a wife who is a virgin of his own people, for he must not father children of the mixed blood—half priestly and half ordinary. For I am the Lord who sanctify him."

We know that Elizabeth and Mary were closely related. If we assume that they were first cousins, then the father of Elizabeth, being a priest and brother, with the sister of Mary's mother or father, would make Elizabeth and Mary cousins, daughters of Aaron.

Luke says that both Zacharias and Elizabeth were very devout people. They worked daily to keep the Laws of God. They had the faith that God saw them as part of the righteous. They lived like God wanted, and they walked blameless before the people of the times. They were fine folks.

Unfortunately, they did not have any children. This was considered one of the greatest afflictions to happen in a Jewish home. It was almost as if it were a curse. Of course, the blame had to be on Elizabeth because everyone knew that a man could get any woman pregnant. In those days, the lack of children was never considered to be the fault of the man. We do not know how old Zacharias and Elizabeth were, but we know that they were elderly. Interestingly, the Koran says that Zacharias was 99 and Elizabeth was 89.

Although Zacharias was well along in years, he continued to perform his priestly duties. Not only was it an honor to work in the temple, but it was also financially rewarding. The Levites usually worked until they were 50. The priests usually continued on into their later years. They would work as long as they thought they had a contribution to make. There were between 20,000 and 25,000 priests living in Palestine at the time of Jesus. They were divided into the courses that served in the temple.

Once the priests making up a particular course had gathered to assume their duties at the temple, they drew lots to determine who would offer different sacrifices, and perform different tasks. There were usually four lots drawn. The first lot were charged with the cleansing of the altar; the second lot killed the sacrifices, sprinkled the blood, removed the ashes, cleaned the candlestick and other items used in the worship service; the third lot offered the incense and was in charge of the casting of the lots; and the fourth brought the sacrifices to the altar. Within each lot, the individual priests went through a long list of duties and ceremonies to be chosen for each day's particular job.

Through the choosing procedure, Zacharias was chosen to burn the incense in the Holy Place. He would have been dressed in white priestly robes, and he would have been bare footed. He would have entered the Holy Place to burn the incense. It would have been a very tense experience for Zacharias. He was as high as a priest could go. Beyond him was the most Holy Place, or the Holy of Holies, which was closed by a heavy, costly curtain. It was supposed to contain the ark of the covenant that was the symbol of the presence of God. Only the High Priest could enter here. We know that the ark of the covenant was not in the most Holy Place at the time of Zacharias. When Roman General Titus entered the most Holy Place he was surprised to find that the Jews worshiped an empty room.

The worshipers throughout the temple were praying as they always did when the incense was burned. The incense was a symbol of prayer. The smell of the incense reminded the people to pray. The people would start to pray as the priest started toward the Holy Place for them. He would enter the room and toss the incense upon a golden altar. A sweet-smelling smoke rose up. This represented the payers and offerings of the people. This ceremony took place on the Sabbath at 9:00 A.M. and 3:00 P.M. The people would remain with bowed heads, facing the Holy Place, in prayer, until the priest came out.

Angels appeared in the Old Testament to a variety of people. Jacob, Moses, Joshua, Gideon, Manoah, Samuel, David, and Daniel all encountered angels. The altar was called the golden altar because it was made of acacia wood overlaid with gold. See Exodus 30:38. It had been more than 400 years, since the time of Malachi, when anyone had reported an encounter with an angel. When people encountered angels, they seemed to be overwhelmed. Manoah was sure he would die when he saw the angel. See Judges 13:22. Daniel almost passed out when he saw an angel. See Daniel 10:8-16.

An angel was standing in precisely the right place, just north of the magnificent golden altar.

When Zacharias saw him, he was terrified. The angel tried to calm him down. He said, "Fear not, your prayers have been answered." The angel told Daniel, "Fear not." The angel then promised Daniel that a great prince would come and deliver Israel from its troubles. The angel here told Zacharias that his prayer to have a son had been answered. He said, "You will have a son." This was the greatest news a Jew could ever hear. The angel then told Zacharias what he would name his son, John, meaning, "Jehovah is gracious." He said that he and his wife would be very joyful because of the birth and many others would rejoice with them. This statement indicates that Zacharias had been praying for a son, not for just himself and Elizabeth, but for all people. If so, Zacharias was a very unselfish man. The angel said John would be great in the sight of the Lord, one of the Lord's great men. Later, Jesus would say that all men ever born, none were ever greater than John.

The angel then described John for his father. He said that John would be a Nazarite, he would never drink wine and never cut his hair. He would be filled with the Holy Spirit.

The laws of the Nazarite are stated in Numbers 6:1-23. There were two kinds of Nazarites, the temporary and perpetual. The first type was far more common. There are only three perpetual Nazarites that we know of: Samson, Samuel, and John the Baptist.

John would be filled with the Holy Spirit from birth. He would be a holy child for a holy cause guided by the Holy Spirit. He would fulfill the prophesy of Malachi 4:6, he would come in the spirit and power of Elijah to turn the hearts of the fathers to the faith of their children. John was like Elijah and he was the bridge between the old and the new dispensation. He did bring the people a new idea. It was one he called upon them to accept like children, to repent and begin life anew with a new faith, a new cleansing, and a new hope.

John would be a herald of the coming Messiah. He would have the power of a prophet of old in reproving sin and preparing the way for the Christ. The Jews believed that Elijah would appear before the Messiah. He would restore Israel to the principles of old. There would be religious upbringing and the people would become righteous preparing the way for the Messiah. A priest like Zacharias could not misinterpret the message the angel was giving him.

Zacharias was amazed. He asked, "How can this be? My wife and I are too old." He was following a great tradition by asking this question. It is the same one Abraham asked when he learned that he would become a father. Zacharias was so skeptical, he was actually asking for a sign that what the angel was saying would come true. The angel wasn't enough, he needed a sign!

The angel told Zacharias that his name was Gabriel and that he stood in the very presence of God. This should have been assurances enough for even the most skeptical person. The Jewish religious tradition held that there were four angels surrounding the throne of God. Gabriel stood before his face and understood 70 languages. Michael was at the right hand of the throne, Uriel at the left, and Raphael behind it. Gabriel was the hero. He was sent on special missions and now he had appeared to Zacharias.

"In your lack of faith, you have asked for a sign." the angel said. "You shall have one. You aren't going to be able to make a sound until the child is born."

This seems like serious punishment for such a simple matter, but consider this: Zacharias had been praying for a son all his life. He was still praying for a son by habit. It was simply part of his prayers. Now, his prayers were being answered and he could not believe it. Obviously, Zacharias did not really expect his prayer to be answered. Each time he said it, he was distrusting God. He would get his sign.

Christians often pray automatic prayers which they do not expect to be answered. They are ritual prayers that we have said so often, we simply keep repeating them. We have no expectation whatsoever of the prayer being answered.

The priest coming out of the Holy Place usually dismissed the people from prayer with a benediction. See Numbers 6:23-26. Zacharias could not give the blessing. Somehow the people understood because he kept making signs. Although he had lost his speech, Zacharias finished his term in the temple.

CHAPTER THREE

MARY EXPECTING, JOHN IS BORN

After Elizabeth became pregnant she stayed indoors. Apparently, she was in constant prayer thanking God for the blessing he had given her. Children were considered a gift from God. The lack of children was considered punishment from God. Therefore, when she was going to have a child, Elizabeth knew that her disgrace was over.

Our prayers are not always denied simply because they are delayed in being answered. The person of faith will hold out to the end always expecting the Lord to answer the prayer. We can imagine that Elizabeth did just this. Now, in the sunset of her life, her prayers were answered so sufficiently that we remember her example today.

Six months after Gabriel appeared to Zacharias, he appeared to Mary. First, he appeared in the Holy Place, then he appeared in Nazareth. Nazareth was not mentioned in the Old Testament, the Talmud, nor in Josephus. Josephus mentions 204 cities and towns in Galilee. Where is Nazareth? No one can be absolutely certain. There is a well where the present Nazareth is. The remainder of the town has been built up around the well as the rebuilt Nazareth.

In Jewish society, the engagement was as important as marriage today. In poor areas like Galilee, the bride was betrothed for her personal character and fitness. Betrothal was a solemn avowal in the presence of witnesses or by written statement, that the parties would be married. The ceremony concluded with a benediction that the couple would be married and blessed. After betrothal, the couple were married for all practical purposes.

The greeting of the angel frightened Mary. She was told by a supernatural being that she was favored by God. She was told God was with her. She was blessed among women. She was told to fear not. The angel let her know he was not there to bring judgment nor condemnation. He was there in grace. She had found favor with the Father. She was going to get pregnant and have a son. He told her to name the child, Joshua, which means, "salvation of Jehovah."

David had contributed to the worship of the people. He had devised systems of worship. He was not only a military leader of the people, he was a spiritual leader of the people. The angel said that Jesus would take over his duties. He would finish the job David started. He would take over David's responsibility.

Mary wanted to know how this could be. Gabriel explained a divine mystery to her. He said that the creator of all life would come upon her and the child born to her would be holy from birth. Mary was assured that her son would be the Son of God. Mary was familiar with scripture. She would have realized that she was part of the fulfillment of Old Testament Messianic prophecies. Mary accepted her responsibility in history. She did not ask for any further sign.

The angel told her about her relative, Elizabeth. Then Mary said to let it be. She was the servant of the Lord. Whatever his will might be, Mary was happy to be part of it and would do what she was called upon to do. The young girl had enormous faith. Once she was over the fright of the supernatural experience, she accepted the message of the angel and welcomed whatever was going to happen. In short, Mary was humble, believing, resigned and ready to do her part. She didn't ask any questions. She didn't express any doubts. She showed enormous courage. She was ready to risk all to please the purposes of the Lord.

When the message had been delivered and Mary had accepted her responsibilities as the mother of the Savior of all mankind, the angel returned to another world, the world from which he came.

From the incidents Luke describes we can learn the lesson that God sends his messengers to the most humble, poor people who love him. The Father gives his finest gifts to the most obscure people in the world. It is like lightening. One never knows where the Lord will act in a decisive way next. Jesus would say that each of us should be as observant as possible.

One thing interesting about the first few verses of Luke is the importance he places on the birth of Jesus Christ. He seems to recognize the Jesus Christ was born at the cross roads *oy* history. The Roman Empire was at its Zenith. Julius Caesar had been assassinated 44 years earlier. Augustus, perhaps the greatest of all the Caesars, was in the triumph of his years. The world was experiencing its greatest prosperity. Religious thought was part of day to day existence. It was the perfect time for the Savior of the world to appear. The birth of Jesus Christ was the most important event in the history of the world. It happened at exactly the right time.

Hannah's song is somewhat different in that it is a song of paradoxes created by God.

It seems Luke could have only received this song from the virgin Mary. The Magnificat has been sung in church services for centuries. It was divided into four verses. The first verse described God's grace; the second verse, his power; the third, his justice, and the fourth, his faithfulness. While the Magnificat is Christian, it is very Jewish in nature. Some have called it a New Testament Psalm.

All the Greek manuscripts of Luke say that Mary said the words of the Magnificat. However, the similarity between Hannah's song and Mary's song is striking indeed. It would not have been copied by Luke. Perhaps some copyist added it. Otherwise, enjoy it as coming from the Blessed Virgin.

Mary went to visit Elizabeth as soon after her experience with the angel as possible. Her motive for the four-day journey was obvious. She would enjoy seeing her relative, but more than that, she wanted to get confirmation of the message she had been given. She wanted to talk with Elizabeth because Elizabeth would understand. She would be able to give Mary very sound advice. She could help Mary plan how she would tell the news to Joseph.

When Mary first saw Elizabeth, or entered her home, she gave the usual Jewish greeting, "The Lord be with you." This greeting triggered joyous delight in both Mary and Elizabeth. The Holy Spirit was on both of them. They were ecstatic and enjoying prophetic powers.

Elizabeth said that Mary was blessed among women. This is similar to a similar expression in the song of Deborah. See Judges 5:24.

"Blessed be Jael, the wife of Heber the Kenite. Yes, may she be blessed above all women who live in tents."

The fact that the women quoted scripture as they talked with each other was not unusual. Both women were closely associated with the priesthood. They knew the Holy Scriptures.

Elizabeth seems to have emptied her soul to Mary when she first saw her. She prophesied everything that had been happening or would happen to Mary. We are not told that Mary had said anything about her experience with the angel. It seems that when Elizabeth first heard Mary's voice, the older woman had a knowing of everything that was happening.

Elizabeth prophesied that Mary would be the mother of the long-awaited Messiah. This information had been given to Elizabeth by the Holy Spirit. She had meditated for months about the purpose God had for her son. She knew that her child was going to be great in the sight of the Lord. Yet, she knew that the child Mary would bear would be the Son of God. Elizabeth was overcome with emotion thinking that she had been so honored to be visited by the Mother of the Messiah. Traditionally, it would have been more appropriate for Elizabeth, no matter her age, to visit Mary.

Elizabeth said that blessed is the person who believes that there will be a fulfillment of the things which have been spoken by the Lord.

Mary said that her soul recognizes, exalts, and praises the Lord. Similar language can be found in Psalms 34:2,3; and Habakkuk 3:18. She rejoiced in God as the source of all things.

Mary was joyous realizing that God had selected her, an obscure young woman, from a lowly family, without power nor wealth. The Lord looked upon her with a special grace and she appreciated this. She knew the importance of what was happening. She knew that future generations would call her blessed. The source of all her joy was the fact that the Lord had chosen her for a divine honor. Although she was joyous, her attitude was humble. God's power had been manifested to her.

Mary's **Magnificat** has been set to music in eight different branches of Christianity. It has been sung thousands of times and continues to be reinterpreted constantly. She concluded her psalm with four verses praising God. She said that God's power had been manifested in her by granting her the great honor he had bestowed upon her.

A few years ago it was terrible when a young girl became pregnant. Some girls left town for six or seven months. As soon as she began to show, she went to visit certain relatives or take care of a sick aunt. When a girl became pregnant in high school during the 40's and early 50's, she was a complete disgrace. She was shunned in her shame. The students made jokes like, "When June became pregnant, 12 boys left town. Most of them were on the football team."

Mary didn't realize that she was about to suffer a worse shame. She was going to be a tainted woman. Neighbors, relatives, and friends were going to talk about her. She was going to be the scandal of the town. She was going to be equated to a harlot. In her innocence, Mary did not think about any of these problems she was going to face. Her faith was totally in the will of the Lord.

The phrases she used are almost all found in the Psalms. The Psalms were written to say or sing the highest praises to God. She was using good judgment by quoting the Psalms. She praised God's great mercy by quoting Psalm 118. "His mercy endureth forever," is the repeated refrain of that Psalm.

She also said words very similar to Psalm 98:10, "Thou has scattered thine enemies with thy strong arm." The Lord's judgment of the proud is mentioned time and again in the Old Testament. She then talks about the Lord exalting the people of low status. This is similar to Hannah's song in I Samuel 2.

Hannah was one of the wives of Elkanah, a Levite who lived at Ramah in Ephraim. She was barren. Peninnah, the other wife, had sons. Elkanah loved Hannah and gave her a double portion of everything. Peninnah was jealous. Hannah prayed constantly for a son. Finally, she promised God that if she could have a son, he would be a Nazarite. Eli saw Hannah praying and accused her of being drunk. He apologized, and when she returned home, Hannah became pregnant, and gave birth to a son. She dedicated him as a Nazirite and named him Samuel.

Mary closed her Magnificat by praising God for his great faithfulness in keeping his promises. She sang about God taking care of the hungry and ignoring those of themselves. In this she was paraphrasing the paradoxical prophesies of Isaiah 65:13.

> "Therefore, thus says the Lord God: 'Behold, my servants shall eat, but you shall be hungry; behold, my servants shall drink, but you shall be thirsty; behold, my servants shall rejoice, but you shall be put to shame.'"

In her innocence Mary never considered that the people of Israel might not accept her future son as the Messiah. She was praising God for making her Son the Savior of Israel. She was overjoyed to be part of God's plan. Failure of that plan was never considered by the Mother of Christ. She could only envision her son as a prince similar to her ancestor David. She could imagine her son sitting up high on David's throne and restoring glory to Israel.

In modern language, Mary said. "Praise God for his mercy. Praise God for his power. Praise God for his justice. Praise God for his faithfulness in fulfilling his promises. And, praise God for his bountiful blessings."

Luke says that after Mary finished her song, she spent three months with Elizabeth. Many scholars believe that the way Luke wrote this portion of the book, he meant that Mary left before Elizabeth had her baby. However, since he mentions the kinspeople of Elizabeth being present when the child was born, he probably includes Mary. The customs of the times, and common-sense, points toward Mary staying with her elderly cousin until after John the Baptist was born. We can imagine the women constantly talking about their unusual experiences. We can believe that Elizabeth told Mary to be patient. The Lord would work in her life just as the angel said he would. She reinforced the faith of Mary and Mary reinforced Elizabeth's faith. The women were good for each other during this time.

The birth of a son was always a cause for celebration in Israel. The birth of John the Baptist was even more a cause of great joy because of the age of his parents, their position in the priesthood, and the remarkable angelic announcements of the birth. The neighbors and relatives gathered as the birth of the child approached and wondered how great he would be. It was obvious that the Spirit of God was upon the baby to be born. It was a joyous occasion for the entire village and they awaited the birth of the child. Everyone celebrated when the blessed event finally arrived.

On the eighth day of his life, the child was circumcised. During the first century, this was a very important ceremony. It was done with great solemnity and usually required at least 10 people to be present as witnesses and pray for the child. In addition to blessing the child from the beginning of his life, they gave the child a name. It was customary to name a boy after his father. Zacharias was dumb, so the gathering named the child after him.

Elizabeth would not have this. She told them to name the child John. Obviously, Zacharias had told her by signs and in writing about the instructions of the angel.

Various forms of writing tablets were in use at the time. One was made of light wood smeared with a dark wax. The writing was done by scratching the wax with a sharp stylus. A writing tablet was handed to Zacharias and he wrote, "His name is John," and all the people were filled with wonder.

"What shall this child be?" they asked.

At the time, the Nation of Israel, and Jews everywhere, were living in a state of fear and anticipation. They feared the power of Rome and they prayed for the deliverance the Messiah would bring. As the local crowd anticipated that the birth of John would have something to do with the coming Messiah, they wondered how the hand of God would work in his life. They thought of Psalm 80:17: "Let thy hand be upon the man of thy right hand."

Immediately, after naming the child, Zacharias was able to speak. He began to praise God for his goodness and mercy. All of his doubts had been removed. He was totally ready to obey the divine message. He began to prophesy to the people.

He said, "Blessed be the Lord God of Israel." These are exactly the words of David when he heard that his son had taken his throne as his successor. See I Kings 1:48.

In the Middle East, the horn was the symbol of great power. When people dressed formerly they often wore a horn as a head ornament. Usually, the horn was colorfully decorated and was part of an attractive head band. The horn was a symbol of glory, of plenty, and strength. John would be a person of great power and he would bring glory to Israel. He would be the forerunner of the Messiah as described by the prophets.

Zacharias said that Israel would be delivered from its enemies. The people thought he was talking about their physical deliverance from Roman bondage. The Holy Spirit, talking through Zacharias, was speaking of a much grander deliverance, the deliverance from death. The Messiah would bring light to the people who sit in the darkness of death's shadow. It is inferred he would deliver his people from sin because the wages of sin is death.

The prophesy of Zacharias begins with a thanksgiving for the appearance of the Messiah. He praised God for the fulfillment of his promises; he expressed joy for the deliverance and redemption the Messiah will bring; then he tells of the work of John the Baptist; and finally, he concludes with the comfort God's people will receive from the light of Christ.

Luke concludes by saying that the child grew in a twofold manner. He grew in body by increasing in size, and he grew in spirit by becoming stronger in the truth. Just as Moses had prepared for his great work in the desert, John remained in the sparsely populated areas of the deserts while he was growing up.

It is very unlikely that John and Jesus knew each other as playmates during their childhood. John was older and lived a life of seclusion. Jesus lived with his parents in Nazareth and learned his father's trade.

At this point Luke has prepared his reader for the birth of Jesus.

CHAPTER FOUR

IN THE DAYS OF CAESAR AUGUSTUS

Gaius Octavius, later known as Gaius Julius Caesar Octavianus, and still later, Caesar Augustus was the first emperor of Rome following the republic which had decayed and disappeared while Julius Caesar was dictator. Julius Caesar was Augustus' great- uncle and adoptive father. After Caesar's death, Augustus was offered absolute power by the Senate and he refused. Instead of being dictator or king, Augustus accepted the title princeps, meaning first citizen. Augustus said he was willing to be known as the first citizen among all Roman citizens.

Gaius Octavius was born September 23, 63 B.C. into a wealthy noble family that had lived in Velletri, southeast of Rome for years. His father had been a Roman Senator who was elected to the high office of praetorship. This was the position immediately below the Consul. His mother was Atia, the daughter of Julia, the sister of Julius Caesar. Caesar sponsored Octavius in public life at a very early age. When he was 12 years old he made his public debut by delivering the funeral speech at his grandmother Julia's funeral. Funeral speeches were very important occasions during the Roman Empire. Such events continued to be great public spectacles until after Abraham Lincoln gave his Gettysburg Address.

When he was 16, Gaius Octavius became a member of the Board of Priests called pontifices. In 46 B.C., he accompanied his uncle during his triumphal procession after his victory in Africa over his enemies in the Civil War. He went with his uncle to Spain. He was in Albania, or Apollonia, in 44 B.C., completing his military education when he learned that Julius Caesar had been assassinated.

Augustus returned to Italy and learned that in his will, Julius Caesar had adopted him and left him as his principal heir. He was only 18 years old. Against the advice of his stepfather and other family members, Augustus decided to take his inheritance and went to Rome. Mark Antony, or Marcus Antonius, had been Caesar's right-hand man. Upon the death of the dictator, he had taken into his possession all of Caesar's papers and assets. He had expected to be the principal heir and he refused to give any of Caesar's funds to Octavius. This forced Octavius to pay the dictator's bequests to the Roman people from funds he could raise. Brutus and Cassius ignored Octavius and withdrew to the east. Cicero, the famous orator, Rome's elder statesman, tried to manipulate the boy, but underestimated his abilities.

By celebrating public games, Octavius became popular with the people and won over enough army legions loyal his uncle to become a very powerful young man. Cicero encouraged the Senate to break with Antony and make Octavius a senator in spite of his age. Octavius joined with Mutina, and Modena, against Antony who had withdrawn to Gaul, or France. When the Consul who commanded the Senate's forces died, Octavius, acting through his troops, forced the Senate to promote him to Consul. He took the name of Gaius Julius Caesar in order to be officially recognized as Caesar's son. He did not follow custom and keep his family name of Octavanus. However, he was called Octavian by the general public until he became known as Augustus.

Octavian settled his differences with Antony and made an ally out of another Caesar supporter, Lepidus, who he promoted to his former post as Chief Priest. On November 27, 43 B.C., the three men were named triumvirs to reconstruct the state. This was the Second Triumvirate. The first had been Julius Caesar, Pompey, and Crassus.

The triumvirs divided the western part of the empire among themselves. They made a list of political enemies and ordered their execution. 300 senators, including Antony's enemy Cicero, were murdered along with 2,000 knights. Julius Caesar was recognized as a god in January 42 B.C. This was a ploy by Octavian which made him the son of god.

Octavian, Antony, and their army crossed the Adriatic to fight the assassins, Brutus and Cassius. Under Antony's leadership, Octavian was very ill, two battles were won and the assassins committed suicide. Octavian agreed that Antony could have the eastern portion of the empire, Lepidus was given Africa, and he returned to Rome.

Immediately, Octavian had problems with his troops. He was unable to pay them the bonus they expected. He paid a portion of the bonuses and made promises as to the balance. He then mobilized the veterans and fought the battle of Perugia against Antony's brother and wife. Sextus Pompeius, the son of Pompey the Great, seized Sicily and the sea routes to Rome. Octavian tried to appease him by marrying his relative, Scribonia. The kinship did not deter Pompeius and Octavian divorced Scribonia due to their incompatibility. Pompeius tried to form an alliance with Antony, but Antony entered into the treaty of Brundisium with Octavian. This gave Octavian all the western empire with the exception of Africa which was left for Lepidus, and Italy which was considered neutral ground.

After Antony spent the winter with Queen Cleopatra in Egypt, he agreed to marry Octavia, the sister of Octavian. Notice how the Romans named their children. There was Julius Caesar and his sister Julia. Octavian's sister was named Octavia. The people of the empire were overjoyed. This marriage promised to end many years of civil war. In 38 B.C. Octavian married an aristocrat, Livia Drusilla. This marriage consolidated his power in the west.

In 37 B.C. Octavian declared war against Sextus Pompeius and immediately lost a series of battles against the strongholds of Pompeius. He made a deal with Mark Antony at Taranto whereby Antony would provide Octavian with ships in return for Octavian furnishing him troops to fight the Parthians and their Median allies. Antony provided the ships, but Octavian never sent the troops. As a result, Antony lost his fight with the Parthians the following year. Octavian put his fleet under the command of a former schoolmate, Marcus Agrippa who was a naval genius. Sextus Pompeius was totally obliterated off Cape Naulochus in Sicily. At that point, the third triumvir, Lepidus, contested Octavian's authority in the west. He was defeated and disarmed by Octavian and stripped of his triumvir office.

Octavian's marriage to Livia began to pay off after two years. The nobles who usually supported Antony switched to Octavian. In confidence, Antony told Octavian the locations where he was going to build cities for his veteran's retirement. Octavian seized these prime locations and built cities for his veterans to live in retirement. This gave him an advantage in recruiting more legionaries to his forces.

Finally, Octavian felt it was time to contest Antony. He started his open contest against his former ally by launching an elaborate religious order worshiping Apollo in contrast to Antony's favorite deity, Bacchus. He adopted the prefix to his name, imperator, which suggests he was a commander of the highest order. He struck his coins without recognizing Anthony. His coins were struck with the emotive name, "Caesar Son of a God."

Between 35 and 33 B.C. Octavian fought three successful campaigns in Illyricum and Dalmatia. With the help of Agrippa, he spent great sums in rebuilding Rome and bringing beauty to the city. He said that he went through Rome covering brick with marble. When he criticized Antony for giving Cleopatra territorial gifts, it was apparent the two men would fight.

In 32 B.C. the triumvirate officially ended. Antony continued to honor the agreement, but Octavian would not. Antony divorced Octavia, and Octavian declared war against Cleopatra in Egypt. He and Agrippa defeated Antony and Cleopatra at Actium. Antony tried to save his ships in hopes of fighting elsewhere, but he got away with only 1/4th. of his fleet. The following year, Antony and Cleopatra committed suicide when it was apparent Octavian was going to capture the entire country. He executed his distant cousin, Cleopatra's son, Ptolemy XV Caesar, or Caesarion, whose father was Julius Caesar, and annexed Egypt. The seizure of Cleopatra's treasury allowed Octavian to pay his veterans their promised bonuses, and made him the ruler of the entire Greco-Roman world.

Slowly and patiently Octavian consolidated his power. He revamped the entire government into a system he called the Roman principiate. This allowed him to reduce the army from 60 legions to 28. The legionaries were mostly Italian and the Praetorian Guards were stationed around Rome and in most the larger cities to keep the peace. He built an efficient fleet and a superb network of roads across the empire. Trade increased and the empire enjoyed unheralded prosperity during a long period of peace.

The Senate was reduced from around 1,000 members to 600 members with Octavian being elected president. He immediately gave the power back to the people further rebuilding the old republican form of government. The people wanted to give him more power, but he refused. In public, he appeared to be a very humble man who was one of the people. In reality, he considered himself a common person, but he was highly intelligent, he was shrewd, devious, selfish, cruel at times.

Bowing to the will of the people, the Senate bestowed upon Octavian the name, "Augustus." This title came from the religious tradition of augury which was the divination of events through omens and casting lots. **Augustus** was a title that contrasted with **humanus**. August was supernatural and the other was human. The title represented a new order recognizing his superiority over the rest of mankind. With the aid of writers such as Virgil, Livy, and Horace, all of whom shared his ideas of governing, Augustus venerated patriotic thought and revived state religions. He repaired temples and reinstituted various ceremonies. He continued military operations on the frontiers in Spain and France.

He kept the peace throughout the empire and the Senate conferred upon him the title of Tribune for life. This gave him the power to convene the Senate as well as represent the common people. The job of Tribune was very ancient in Rome. The Tribune was the direct representative of the plebs. Augustus now became the supporter of the interests of the common and poor people. He made landlords repair their hovels and he established a system of justice whereby the common man was equal to persons born of higher rank. He prepared Agrippa to take over government should one of his frequent illnesses kill him.

By 19 B.C., when Augustus was 44 years old, he made peace with the Parthians, and Agrippa had completed the subjugation of Spain. Augustus began to travel around the empire. Everywhere he went, reorganization followed, governments were made stronger, people were given more freedom, laws were passed and the general welfare was improved. He encouraged marriage, discouraged adultery, preached morality and encouraged thrift among the people.

By 17 B.C. Augustus had begun to implement his plan as to who would be his successor. He knew he needed rest so he trained a large staff of knights and freedmen. They were the beginning of what we know of today as civil service. They were ordinary common people and ex-slaves who ran the empire. He centralized the monetary system of the empire. He codified the laws and set up a system of taxation. He had a poll tax which was paid by every citizen in the empire, and a land tax which was paid on all the farms. Although everyone was taxed, the taxes were so low that trade continued to flourish.

In 12 B.C., Lepidus died. This enabled Augustus to finally become head of the Roman religion. He became the pontifex maximus, or Chief High Priest. He sent his nephew Tiberius against Yugoslavia and Hungary, while he sent his brother Drusus to finish conquering the Germanic tribes. As all the other people Augustus trusted began to die off, including Agrippa, he began to seriously groom Tiberius as his successor. He adopted him as his son and made him an equal in everything other than his personal prestige. For all practical purposes, he turned the government over to Tiberius and his freedmen civil servants.

The year Jesus Christ was born Augustus Caesar participated in government as he pleased. He was sick so much that when he could govern he participated only in those things that intrigued him. The rest of the time he was inaccessible. He was 63 years old, and he was an old man. He had a few worn yellow teeth left, and he had constant kidney trouble. He did not sleep well. He could barely see out of his left eye, and he had a chronic cough and breathing problems. He was five feet four inches tall, he was the most powerful man on earth, and perhaps the most powerful ruler in all history. Approximately eighty million people were under his direct dominion and control.

He lived half way up one of Rome's seven hills in an aristocratic section of town. He had a commanding view of the city. His religion was basically a superstition based upon fortune tellers, signs and dreams. When Jesus Christ was born Augustus had been in power twenty-eight years. He had consolidated all power. During this time, he had beautified the city. He talked his son-in-law, Marcus Agrippa, into putting up the money to build the great temple, the Pantheon.

Still, Rome had slums which defied the imagination. Three quarters of a million people were jammed into a six square mile area. The slums smelled terrible, they were filthy, poverty ridden, overcrowded, pest infested, and very dangerous. Most of the landlords-built tenements one on top the other until ten or twelve stories high. The shacks were built on poles. The poet Juvenal said,

> "Rome is supported on pipe stems, and matchsticks. It's cheaper, so, for the landlord to shore up his ruins, patch up the old cracked walls, and notify the tenants they can sleep secure, though the beams are in ruins above them."

There was always the possibility that the town would go up in smoke. Several times Rome burned. Each time the holocaust killed thousands of people. Then plague and illness after the fire deaths took their toll. Augustus had developed and trained an efficient fire brigade which successfully kept fire damage at a minimum. He rebuilt great sections of the slums.

He brought peace to a devastated world. The people loved him. He was a benevolent despot. He became the imperator, or boss. He personally ruled France, Egypt, Syria, and Spain. All legions in these areas were under his personal command and composed most of the Roman army. The remaining legions wanted to be personally commanded by Augustus. He always paid large bonuses and provided for an enjoyable retirement for his troops.

The people wanted to worship him, but he would not tolerate this much adoration. He insisted that prayers to him should be joined with the real gods of ancient Rome. He reacted in horror when someone called him "Lord." One tribute people repeated about Augustus was:

> "Your possession is equal to what the sum can pass. Nor do you reign within fixed boundaries, nor does another dictate to what point your control reaches; but the sea like a girdle lies extended, at once in the middle of the civilized world and of your influence."

Augustus insisted that the nations pay the Roman tax to support the state. He kept whatever portion of the treasury he desired. Fortunately, he was a tight wad and wanted very little from the country he truly loved.

Quirinius had proven his unwavering loyalty to Augustus and was rewarded by being made governor of Syria. It was probably Autumn 5 A.D. when Augustus decided that he would take a census of the empire the following year, in 6 A.D. In so doing he would collect the poll tax. He had set up a spoils system which worked efficiently. He paid everybody from the tax collector up a percentage of the take.

Luke is obviously incorrect when he places the birth of Jesus at the time Quirinius was governor of Syria. Jesus was born in approximately 4 B.C. The census taking place during the time of Quirinius was at least ten years later.

Herod the Great died in 4 B.C. At the time of a ruler's death, it was customary for a new king or governor to take a census to find out how many people lived within the kingdom and to collect the head tax. The census Mary and

Joseph were enrolled in when Jesus was born was the census of Herod's shortly before his death, or that of his sons upon the death of their father.

Luke dates the beginning of the ministries of Jesus and John the Baptist as 29 A.D. had Jesus been born when the census of Quirinius was taken in A.D. 6. He would have been 23 years old and this would be entirely too young for the rest of his ministry. Matthew says that Jesus was born when Herod the Great was king. Herod was still king when Matthew said that he slaughtered the innocent children two years later in Bethlehem. This would result in Jesus being born in 6 B.C. 4 B.C. appears to be the better year as this results in the beginning of his ministry when he was 33.

At the time Jesus was ten years old, a Jew named Judas the Galilean put together a group of zealots and sicarii, or daggermen, and challenged the Roman authority of Palestine. He attacked the royal arsenal at Sepphoris, four miles from Nazareth. Judas the Galilean said that it was a religious duty for all Jews to revolt against Rome. He said that the required oath to the emperor was incompatible with the absolute sovereignty of God as laid down by the Covenant. He was preaching insurrection. A Pharisee named Zadok joined his organization and the movement appeared to be ready for open revolt. The high priest Joazar swayed the public against them. This was an open change among the Jewish aristocracy. The priestly group was now going to cooperate with Rome the way it had always cooperated with Herod.

Joazar's cooperation made him too pro-Roman. The general public was determined to be rid of him and of the entire Boethus family. He was succeeded by Ananus and his family who controlled the office for the next thirty-five years. Jewish tradition preserves the public's disdain for both families in the saying:

> "Woe is me because of the house of Boethus! Woe is me because of their slaves! Woe is me because of the house of Ananus! Woe is me because of their whisperings!"

It was because of such tumultuous times that any new speaker, outside the accepted Pharisees and Sadducees, was closely watched by the king or government officials.

CHAPTER FIVE

JEWISH HISTORY LEADING TO JESUS

Joseph was a member of the family of King David. He was required to return to his ancestral home of Bethlehem to enroll in the census. Mary was about due. It was a long, hard, 90-mile, five-day trip, and probably hastened the birth of Jesus Christ.

Bethlehem was located five miles southwest of Jerusalem. It was 2,550 feet above sea level in the Judean hill country. It was on the main highway to Egypt. In Jacob's time it was called, Ephrath or fruitful. It was the burial place of Rachel, Boaz and Ruth. See Genesis 35:16,19; 48:7. Boaz lived in Bethlehem. His Great-grandson, David was anointed king by Samuel there. From that time on it was called the City of David. At one time it was occupied as a Philistine army garrison. See II Samuel 23:14-16. Later, it was fortified by Rehoboam. See II Chronicles 11:6.

In Jeremiah's time, Bethlehem was the home of the caravan inn named Chimham. This was the usual starting place for people going to Egypt. At the time of the birth of Jesus, it was still a town known for its inns. It is believed that Jesus was born in a cave close to the village. This is the spot where the Church of the Nativity was built by Constantine's mother in 330 A.D.

Approaching Bethlehem at the time of Jesus a traveler would see a cluster of boxlike, whitewashed buildings on the top of a low but rather steep ridge.

There may have been as many as 300 people living in the town. It was a commercial center where the travelers bound for Egypt bought their provisions for the trip.

For the Jews Bethlehem had a special significance. It was the place where, according to the prophet Micah, the Messiah would be born.

Joseph and Mary would have approached the city with all their provisions tied on their donkey. Joseph would have been a strong robust man in the prime of his life. Mary was probably a 15-year-old teenager. They would have walked through the entrance to the town, past Roman sentries on guard duty, into a city of dust and crowds. The place was jammed with people of all descriptions. The town square was the market place and people were busy. Peasants and craftsmen came to sell their products. Wealthy Jews from Egypt, Rome, Greece and other points were purchasing. It was a noisy bustling place.

Ordinarily, any visitor could find some sort of accommodations in Bethlehem. But now the town was bursting at the seams due to everyone coming back to be counted. Three feet of every flat roof was occupied. There was absolutely no space. Joseph instantly knew he would have trouble finding accommodations.

The historical events leading up the first Christmas, or the birth of the Messiah, accelerated to a fever pitch beginning two centuries before Jesus. The Maccabean revolt, which occurred from 167 B.C. until 142 B.C., ended the Syrian domination of Palestine.

The intense messianic movement began after the Syrian King Antiochus Epiphanes (Antiochus IV), conquered Israel. Antiochus was determined to stamp out the Jewish religious tradition. He was going to Hellenize Jerusalem. The Jews considered him to be the "Abomination of Desolation" predicted in the Book of Daniel. Antiochus issued repressive orders in every town in Palestine. All places of worship were converted to Greek deities. The Samaritans were compelled to dedicate their shrine of Mount Gerizim to Olympian Zeus. There were savage persecutions and many people took great pride in religious martyrdom. One Martyr shouted to Antiochus IV:

> "I, like my brothers, surrender my body and my life for the laws of our fathers. I appeal to God to shew mercy speedily to his people, and by whips and scourges to bring you to admit that he alone is God!"

Antiochus IV sacrificed a pig on the altar of the temple in Jerusalem. This defiled the entire temple, making it unclean for worship by the Jews. His sacrilege of pagan worship and bringing temple prostitutes to Jerusalem, so outraged the population that all Israel became a tender box that was ready for revolt.

In 168 B.C., Mattathias of Modein, an aged priest, refused to participate in a pagan sacrifice. He then killed an apostate Jew, a royal commissioner, who was willing to take his place and make the sacrifice to a heathen god. Mattathias then tore down the sacrificial altar and fled to the hills with his family. This began the most successful war of independence ever mounted by the Jews. Mattathias was a member of the priestly clan of Joarib, not of the house of

Aaron, which would have enabled his family to claim the Davidic high priesthood.

In the mountains Mattathias became the arch-hero of resistance movements. He was the perfect example of ruthless zeal and patriotism. He was a religious leader in the manner of Phineas, grandson of Aaron, the high priest of Moses' time, who killed a Jew and his foreign woman with a single spear thrust for worshiping more than one God. See Numbers 25:7-8.

Early fighting claimed two of his sons, Eleazar and John, and Mattathias died in 166 B.C. The remaining brothers, Judas, Jonathan, and Simon each in turn led the revolt against the Seleucid domination. Seleucid empire consisted of Greeks ruling Syria. Due to his successes in guerilla warfare, Judas was given the name Maccabee, or Hammerer. The clan also took on their old family name of Hasmon. They were called the Maccabees or Hasmonaeans.

Judas the Maccabee was a brilliant military strategist. He organized an army of fighting Galileans and in quick succession he overthrew the Syrian generals Apollonius, Seron, Gorgias, and the regent Lysias. In actual fact, his battles were the most stirring chapter in Israelite history. He was a far greater general than David, Gideon, Joshua, or any other Jewish military leader.

After three years of bloody battles, Judas eventually formally cleansed the temple of Syrian pollution in 165 B.C. The festival celebrating this event is called Hanukkah, and is celebrated by Jews in early December.

Judas, whose Jewish name was Yehudah, was the perfect example of the Jewish developing concept of the Messiah. Yet, he was never considered to be the messiah. He was never considered to be high priest because of his blood line. In 161 B.C. he entered into a peace treaty with Rome, and later, Greece. He even entered into treaties with various cities around the Roman Empire. Like his brothers before him, he was eventually killed in battle.

Simon Maccabeus, the last surviving brother, won freedom for all Palestine from the Seleucids.

In 141 B.C. Simon Maccabeus, who was the second son of Mattathias, and the older brother of Judas, called a meeting of all the nobles, priests, and elders of the country to Jerusalem. At this meeting, Simon had himself elected as the high-priest, military commander, and civil governor of the Jews forever, or until there should arise a faithful prophet to take his place. He was the only person in Palestine authorized to wear the purple. With this act, the high-priest-hood became hereditary in the family of Simon. The offices of high priest, military commander and civil governor were declared to be heredity offices within the Hasmonaeans.

This began the Hasmonaean dynasty. Simon brought peace to a country that had been dominated for years. He instituted a central coinage and ushered in a period of prosperity seldom seen in Israel. In 135 B.C. Simon was murdered along with two of his sons by his son-in-law, Ptolemy, governor of Jericho. He and his sons were at a banquet while he was visiting the cities of his kingdom. Ptolemy wanted his father-in-law's position of power.

Simon's son, John Hyrcanus, came to power and held the positions of his father through force. While engaged in a war with Ptolemy, he was attacked by Antiochus VII and was forced to take refuge in the fortress city of Jerusalem.

He negotiated a peace settlement upon the payment of an indemnity and an annual tribute to Antiochus. He confirmed the alliance his father had with Rome and captured Samaria and Idumaea. Although he remained in power only one year, John Hyrcanus left the Jewish nation in a position of great independence and influence. He was succeeded by his brother Alexander Jannaeus.

Because of his Sadducean policies, Jannaeus was out of favor with the Pharisees who rose in revolt. He brought savage revenge on the Pharisees and was followed power by his widow, Salome Alexandria who ruled from 76 B.C. until 67 B.C. She was a successful ruler because she ruled in accordance with the ideals of the Pharisees. Her youngest son, Aristobulus, captured 20 towns in a civil war with his brother Hyrcanus II, who was a weakling. Salome died during the conflict between her sons and Hyrcanus had to retire in favor of his brother.

A new and disturbing element now entered into Jewish politics in the person of the Idumaean Antipater. He made great mischief between the brothers. In 65 B.C., Antipater persuaded Aemilius Scaurus, Legate in Syria of Pompey, to interfere in Palestine. The siege of Jerusalem by Pompey followed in 63 B.C. and the Jews became vassals of Rome. Repeated attempts were made by the Hasmonaeans and their patriotic supporters to throw off the Roman Yoke. In 40 B.C., the Parthians set up as king Antigonus who was the sole surviving son of Aristobulus. He was executed by Mark Anthony in 37 B.C. and the Hasmonaean dynasty came to an end.

The Hasmonaeans continued to have some influence in Judea in some form or another until 34 B.C. when Herod, with the help of Rome, came to power.

And this ended the most glorious era of Jewish history, including the time of King David.

Thanks to the Maccabees, the Jews had enjoyed their greatest freedom from 142 B.C. until 63 B.C. when the Romans, under Pompeii conquered Israel after the bloody fall of Jerusalem. This was the year Augustus was born.

The atrocities resulting from the siege of the Holy City and the Roman domination of the land caused a distinct shift in the Jewish concept of the Davidic Messiah.

All Jews had been happy to be free after the success of the Maccabees. Unfortunately, once peace had returned to the land, the leaders of the Jewish faith resented the new Maccabean-Hasmonaean dynasty because the brothers had not descended from King David. On religious grounds alone, the Maccabees could not herald in the kingdom promised by the prophets. Therefore, no successor to the Maccabees could be the promised Messiah. Additionally, both Jonathan and Simon Maccabee had dared to promote themselves to high priest without being descended from the priestly line of Zadok as required by I Kings 1:26:

"But Zadok the priest and Bennaiah and Solomon and I weren't invited,"

And II Samuel 8:17

"Zadok (son of Ahibut) and Ahimelech (son of Abiathar) were the High Priests, and Seraiah was the king's private secretary."

Once the religious leadership accepted the fact that the Maccabees were not descendants of King David, nor his High Priest Zadok, they saw their saviors as nothing more than power-hungry interlopers, who selfishly foisted themselves into the political and religious leadership of Israel.

Opposition to the Maccabees was very strong among men who considered themselves to be pious Jews. The question of the proper bloodline of the high priesthood became so intense that society reached a flashpoint of rebellion against the Maccabees. The Pharisees, as a political party, officially broke with the Hasmonaean-Maccabean regime in 134 B.C. They announced that they were awaiting a new Messiah. Their hope was for an ideal, non- Maccabean king. This anticipated Messiah would be a descendant of King David. Then, they added two new characteristics the Messiah would have: First, he would be the ruler of the entire world, not just Israel. Second, he would arrive just before the end of the world. In short, the Messiah awaited by the Pharisees would be an emperor of the world who would come to power heralding the end of time.

Before the Babylonian Exile, the term "Messiah" had meant the "anointed one," and referred to any Davidic king of the country. This "Messiah" had none of the supernatural connotations later Jews and Christians would give him. Before the exile, the Messiah was a political and military leader, a man who was nothing more than a human being who was recognized as the chosen agent of God's will on earth.

As a sign of his being God's representative, the Messiah would be anointed with oil by a prophet or priest. When the person was anointed, he became the "Son of God." This term did not indicate he was divine, but only that he was

God's special agent on earth. The prophets called for an ideal man, the future Messiah-king, would be called "Wonderful, Counselor, Almighty God, Everlasting Father, and Prince of Peace." This reference from Isaiah 9:6 describes a mortal human being, a national leader who would have the theocratic role as God's representative on earth.

Although the Old Testament mentions the anointed one on several occasions, it does not mention a Messiah. Jeremiah said in 23:6

> "In his days Judah will be saved, and Israel will dwell securely. And this is the name by which he will be called: 'The Lord is our righteousness.'"

The Messiah of the Pharisees absorbed the traditional traits of the awaited Anointed One of history as well as the other powers they ascribed to him. Their idea of the Messiah was not just another king of Israel, but rather the final universal emperor.

He would not descend from Heaven, he would be born like any other person. His special significance was his appearance to make Israel the ruler of the world and the coming of the end of time.

The Essenes, or Holy Ones, were resolutely against the Maccabees. When the Hasmonaeans took over the high priesthood, around 142 B.C., approximately 4,000 Essenes left the towns and villages and went into the desert and began to live separately in settlements they created. Their largest enclave was the colony at Qumran near the Dead Sea. The Essenes lived a simple life sharing everything in common. They were mostly unmarried men who adopted other believer's children for training. They did not participate in temple worship but had their own purification rites. They were avid students of the Jewish Scriptures and looked forward to a purely religious Messiah. They maintained that their leader, a person called the "Righteous Teacher," was not the Messiah, but he was a living sign that the world had entered its last days and the true Messiah was about to appear. They had a sacrament whereby they drank wine and ate bread in anticipation of the coming Messianic banquet.

In 110 B.C. many Pharisees fled the towns and villages and joined the Essenes because of what they considered persecution by the Hasmonaeans. They brought with them their ideas about the political Messiah. As a result, almost 25 years before the birth of Jesus, the people at Qumran began to expect two Messiahs. One was a high priest descended from Aaron and the other was a world emperor who was descended from David. Their scriptural authority for this belief came from Zechariah 4:12-14:

> "And a second time I said to him, 'What are these two branches of the olive trees, which are beside the two golden pipes from which the oil is poured out?' He said to me, 'Do you not know what these are?' I said, 'No, my lord.' Then he said, 'These are the two anointed ones who stand by the Lord of the whole earth.'"

Shortly before Jesus was born, there was another, almost overwhelming, expectation which swept throughout the Jewish religious tradition. This was the anticipation of the prophet who would appear immediately before the end of the world. This prophet was supposed to be Elijah who had been swept up to heaven 800 years earlier. They seized the authority for this concept from the prophet Malachi. In Malachi 4:5 it is said:

> "Behold, I will send you another prophet like Elijah before the great and terrible day of the Lord comes. And he will bring the fathers and the children together again, to be of one mind and heart, for they will know that if they do not repent, I will come and smite the land with a curse."

The three decades before the birth of Jesus Christ witnessed Jewish thought in transition. Most Jews believed the end of the world was at hand. The world had gone as far as it could go, life as the people knew it was over. Before the world could end, the Messiah had to appear. Therefore, they anticipated the appearance of Elijah to prepare the land for the appearance of the Jewish world king and savior of the Jews.

If the entire matter seems confusing, it was. It was a dream of the end of the world, which contained the hope that the Messiah would redeem Israel. The prophet would call upon the people to repent and turn to God as the prophets of old had done. The people would accept the redemption offered by the Messiah, and he would bring peace to the earth. The Jews would be the leader of the world under the direction of their Messiah. When peace finally came to all the earth, the end of time would occur.

Jesus was born in the year 3755 on the Jewish calendar. If one looked throughout Jewish history, a more convenient time for the appearance of a Messiah could not have happened. He came at the crossroads of history and at the time of the highest Messianic expectations among Jews.

The New Testament concept of the Messiah was developed from all the Old Testament descriptions of the Savior. The suffering servant who made vicarious atonement for the nation through his passion and death. Jesus combined the concept of the suffering, dying and glorified Servant of the Lord with that of the Son of Man who would return on the clouds of heaven.

Jesus called himself the Son of Man. This name was used not so much to express his humanity, but to express a paradox. While he was human, he is at the same time a man who recognized the supernatural powers of the kingdom of God. Such a person pre-existed before Abraham.

"Before Abraham," Jesus said, "the Son of Man was." As the Son of God, Jesus said he possessed the power of God's authority over his creation.

As with any other world changing event, the birth of Jesus Christ has resulted in a great deal of speculation. We don't know the exact date he was born. Matthew says that the birth of Jesus was told to Joseph in a dream. Luke says that the news was conveyed directly to Mary by an angel. According to Luke, Mary and Joseph traveled from their home in Nazareth to Bethlehem to take part in the Roman census. According to Matthew, they were already living in Bethlehem. They were obliged to leave when Herod began to kill all the boy babies in Bethlehem. There is absolutely no historical corroboration that Herod ever ordered the killing of any babies. According to Mark, Jesus seems to have always lived in Nazareth.

Why do we have problems with the two conflicting nativity stories? First, these stories result in Jesus being different from us. Jesus said he was exactly like everyone else, all of us are one, and there is only one. Second, the nativity stories sit uncomfortably in two gospels, Matthew and Luke. The stories are replete with errors without any attempt to correct the many misconceptions they may cause. Many facts seem to have been added to the books by a later copyist. Once the miraculous stories are told, they are never mentioned again. Yet they are so startling that Christians revisit them each year. Why not? We celebrate Christ mass and we can't even prove Nazareth even existed as a place at the time Jesus was born. If it did exist, it was the smallest, and one of the most insignificant places in Galilee. The earliest Nazareth appears in Jewish literature was during the seventh century A.D.

Both nativity writers went to great lengths to tie Jesus to the line of King David. Jesus Christ was further removed from the original Jewish King David than we are from William the Conqueror. Any genealogy going that far back in time is purely conjecture.

Probably the greatest thing about Christ's Mass is the love it requires us to show to each other. The Jesus season is a time for loving, for peace, for worship, for joy, for giving, and for receiving. It is a time of sociological interchange when we interact with each other on our very best behavior. This makes Christ's Mass the most favored time of year. It always lets us know what we have the potential to be with each other.

If you knew that you could change the world forever, for good, and if you knew you could point your future brothers and sisters toward a closer relationship with the Father of all, would you be willing to be born in a manger, a cave like stable to do it? Of course, you would. Jesus Christ did.

CHAPTER SIX

THE BIG DAY HAS ARRIVED

After the young couple arrived in the village of Bethlehem, they discovered that Mary was in labor and about to deliver her child. Luke wrote his Gospel in such a way as to make sure it is understood that Jesus was the first child born to Mary. Although some Christian traditions hold that Mary was forever a virgin, the text appears to point the way to other children to be born of Mary. Mark talks about Jesus' sisters and we know he had brothers, James and Joses. So Jesus Christ was the first of several children in the family of Joseph Ben Heli, the carpenter from Nazareth.

Christian tradition holds that Mary wrapped her baby with her own hands. It was the custom in Palestine at the time for young mothers to wrap their new born babies in a single piece of cloth until the baby looked similar to a little live mummy. The young couple could not possibly have obtained rooms in the successor to the well-known Chimham Inn which had existed in ancient times. The Bethlehem Inn was the Hilton of the times. It is believed that this inn consisted of a large courtyard in the center of a three-sided structure which had two balconies under roof. The courtyard was where travelers brought their animals and beasts of burden. There was a feeding area for a number of animals at once. When crowded, several chutes or stalls were built on the top of a small incline. The animals were unloaded, led into the chutes which directed the animal down the other side of the incline to food and water. There were small elevated walkways about two feet higher than the manger area where small rooms were located. Each room had at least one tiny window near the ceiling of the room for much needed ventilation. The place was stuffy and smelled strong like a barnyard. If a traveler had a room on the first floor, after feeding and watering the livestock, like most guests, he brought his animals into his room with him. People wanted to be sure their most valuable possessions were not stolen nor damaged. Also, they wanted all their valuable goods kept together. The wealthier people slept in the upstairs rooms alone while servants or slaves slept with their animals. They slept either in the center of the inn, or just outside the inn, but still on the grounds.

The innkeeper provided only space and water. The traveler provided his bedding, food, fodder for his animals, cooking utensils, and what other comforts he brought with him or bought in the village. Unless a person was rich, travel was the worst thing a person could undertake. A person taking a thirty-mile trip would put all of his affairs in order before he left. Often, when a person left on a trip, he would never be seen again.

Joseph inquired of the innkeeper where he might find space where his baby could be born. If anyone in town would know, the innkeeper would know. He was an innovative fellow. He knew that there was not enough room anywhere in town for a woman to have a baby. People were sleeping in all public places, all rooftops had been rented, and people were sleeping on stairs and places where animals were kept. However, he did not want a penny to get away during this windfall time of high finance. So, he rented space in a cave near the inn which he used as an additional stable for more affluent guests. Mangers were feeding troughs for cattle which were usually made of stone, or carved out of one large stone. They were just the right size for a baby to sleep in.

Contrary to what some believe, it wasn't poverty nor a lack of hospitality that resulted in Joseph finding a space in the cave. It was simply a lack of room. Joseph was upper-middle class of his day. He was educated, a tradesman, and generally well to do. The census had brought the crowd to Bethlehem. Although they were all somewhat related, there were too many people and too little space. It was one huge family reunion.

Usually, the first spaces rented in the town were the more comfortable large rooms in the individual homeowner's homes. The villagers were familiar with renting space to travelers. It was a money-making venture that they engaged in whenever possible. They were carrying on a family tradition that had taken place for centuries.

Justin Martyr, one of the earliest Christian theologians, was born in Shechem and lived all his life in Palestine. Around 132 A.D., he said that Jesus was born in a cave at Bethlehem. In 330 A.D., Helena, the mother of Constantine I the Great, built the church of the Nativity over the cave where tradition has it Jesus was born. Helena was the perfect person to build this church as she had managed an inn at Drepanum in Bithynia before marrying Constantius I Chlorus. In 293 A.D., he discovered her so that he might marry Theodora, stepdaughter of the emperor Maximian as a Caesar. His and Helena's son later became emperor. When Constantine became emperor at York in 306 A.D., he immediately named his mother as empress-dowager. Helena became a Christian and devoted her life to her oldest grandson Crispus, who was executed in 326.

Crispus was actually Flavius Julius Caesar. He was educated as a Christian by the writer Lactantius Firmianus. He was given the title Caesar on March 1, 317, and became the ruler of France. In 324 he commanded the Roman fleet and won a decisive victory at the Hellespont. He was traveling with his father Constantine to Rome to celebrate his 20th. year as emperor when he was executed in Pola, Yugoslavia. He had been accused by his stepmother Fausta of attempting to seduce her. Soon thereafter, Fausta was denounced as a liar by Helena. This resulted in Constantine ordering the execution Fausta. This double tragedy in her family hurt Helena so much that she could not tolerate life as she had known it. She set out on a pilgrimage to the Holy Land to find peace.

As Helena visited the holy sites in the life of Jesus she had monuments erected, or markers established, so others might locate the sites in the centuries to follow. She built the church of the Nativity and the church of the Ascension which pilgrims still visit by the millions. Coins bearing her name were struck in her honor in 330 A.D. During the building of the church on Golgotha, it was claimed that she discovered the cross of Jesus and preserved it. This caused a number of legends to spring up concerning the cross. Eventually, she was elevated by the church as Saint Helena and made "equal to the Apostles." She is buried in Constantinople, or modern Istanbul.

The actual manger cave is located in solid rock twenty feet beneath the great choir loft of the church built by Helena. The site can be reached by a narrow passageway. Hepworth Dixon, a later Christian historian, maintains that the cave was not only the birthplace of Jesus, but was once owned by Boaz and occupied by David. Other sites have been venerated as the birthplace of Jesus, but the cave marked by Helena is the most authentic and is recognized in tradition as the place where Jesus was born.

The actual date of the birth of Jesus is unknown. There have been arguments made by theologians to support every month of the year. April 20th. and May 20th., 4 B.C., are the more popular dates. We do know that he was not born on December 25th. The tradition of this date came about in the second or third century in Rome to compete with the pagan celebration of the worship of Saturn, or the disappearing sun, called Saturnalia.

Shepherds in the area of Bethlehem generally lived in the open air all year long. They were the true outdoorsmen, rarely spending anytime in a home. Although they might be handsome young men, as a result of their lifestyle, they were generally considered to be unclean. They rarely bathed, they did not own good clothing and they smelled ripe.

They dressed in sheepskin with the wooly side next to their bodies. The tanned leather side of the skin was oiled slick to shed rain. Their equipment consisted to a bag made out a goat's skin with the legs tied together. In the bag the shepherd kept his food, personal items, and extra clothing, if any. He carried a sling to protect himself and the sheep from animals. He carried a rod about 30 inches long with a knob on one end for additional protection. He had a staff with a crook in one end to snare the stray sheep, or sheep that did not follow his instructions. Additionally, he usually had some sort of musical instrument, such as a flute made of reeds, to entertain himself and keep the herd quiet. He slept in his clothing using whatever shelter he could find. He knew each of his sheep by name and each of the sheep knew each shepherd's voice.

He usually herded them into a fold at night for protection so he could get some rest. The shepherds kept several sheep herds together in the fold at night to prevent theft, killings by wolves, leopards, foxes, wild dogs, and jackals.

Frequently, the slopes of the hills near Bethlehem were used to graze the sheep that would be used as sacrificial offerings in the temple in Jerusalem. Whether the shepherds were tending sacrificial sheep for religious purposes, or village sheep of several owners, they would have been like everyone else, looking for the Messiah.

The shepherds slept in short shifts to protect the herd throughout the night when it was most vulnerable. In case the herd was attacked by a wild animal, all the shepherds fought off the attack together. Although shepherding was considered an honored profession because David had been a shepherd, individual shepherds were not highly regarded by society in general.

Where families had only a few sheep, they would often join together with relatives and graze their sheep together. These sheep were brought back into the village or settlement at night and herded into a common fold owned by the family. These shepherds were not professional herders. They were basically farmers who kept sheep as a money crop. One or two family members would tend the sheep while the rest of the villagers worked in the fields all day.

We do not know what kind of shepherds were tending the flocks the night Jesus was born. Probably, the gospel writers are referring to professional shepherds who lived with the sheep year around. They watched the skies and night and participated in the myths associated with the clear heavens. They also discussed the coming promised One and hoped for a better tomorrow.

For centuries before Christ people had imagined angels, part bird and part man, a being that could fly. This was one of the most beautiful and fanciful things imaginable. Flying, by any manner or means, was beyond the conception of people. Therefore, any humanoid who could fly had to have a special significance. They named such beings angels from the Greek, angelos, meaning messenger.

In the Jewish, Islamic, and Christian traditions angels are beings which are inferior to God, but superior to man. They came about in the belief in the existence of intermediary beings between God and man, beings that brought direct messages from God to people. In Old Testament times people believed there were so many angels that God was called the "Lord of hosts". The hosts being unnumbered angels. See I Samuel 1:3-11.

An angel was the guard of the entrance to the garden of Eden after the fall of man. See Genesis 3:24. Their appearance was in human form. See Genesis 18:2,16. Angels play large roles in the books of Job, Daniel, Ezekiel and Tobit. In Jude 9, there is a hierarchy of angels. We learn their personal names, Michael, Gabriel, and Raphael. In the Old Testament most angels are referred to as cherubim and seraphim who attended God's throne. See Ezekiel 1, and Isaiah 6:2-6. Two cherubim were carved to guard the ark with their overshadowed wings. This was the mercy seat and represented God's throne on earth. See Exodus 25:18-21.

At the time of the birth of Jesus the Sadducees refused to believe in the existence of angels though the Pharisees and Essenes believed in them as never before. They wrote about them, depicted them in art, and decorated the temple with them. Believers were looking for angels on a constant basis. Angels are associated with Jesus from his birth through his baptism, agony, resurrection and ascension. Jesus frequently talked about angels and suggests the idea of a guardian angel for children in Matthew 18:10:

> "Beware that you don't look down upon a single one of these little children. For I tell you that in heaven their angels have constant access to my father."

The Apostle Paul divided angels into seven groups, angels, archangels, principalities, powers, virtues, dominions and thrones. See I Thessalonians 4:16, Romans 8:38, Ephesians 1:21, Colossians 1;16, and 2:15. The Book of Revelation carries angels to a new height in Christian theology.

The official cult of angels has been a phenomenon which reached its highest point in the Christian tradition. The cult probably began in the 9th. century B.C., during the rule of the Assyrian Ashurbanipal II at Nimrud. Christianity has placed great devotion toward Michael, the powerful angel warrior. Shrines in his honor began to appear as early as the 4th. century A.D. and continues down through today. Female angels began to be recognized in the early Renaissance Period. And one angel, Cupid, according to legend, refused to be baptized. He is a cherub who is supposed to be earthbound until the end of time.

St. Augustine believed in angels but said they possessed purely spiritual bodies, and were not physical in any aspect of their existence. Gregory the Great taught that angels are pure intelligence and materialized and demateriaized before people. Jesus said that angels rejoice when someone repents and turns to the Father, and bears the souls of the dead to Heaven.

As the shepherds were tending their flocks on the hillside, an apparition of angels appeared to them in the night sky. No one else saw the miraculous event. The shepherds realized that they were involved in a glorious event and they were scared. Perhaps they thought judgment day had appeared.

One angel first appeared and quieted the fears of the simple shepherds as Gabriel had done with Mary. Instead of bringing vengeance to mankind, the angel said that he brought good tidings of great joy for all the earth. He announced that the Messiah, the anointed of the Lord, had been born in Bethlehem. This was just as the prophets had predicted. He then gave shepherds a sign. He told them that they would find the child lying in newborn cloth in a manger. The sign distinguished the promised Messiah from other children which might be in Bethlehem at the time. Though ordinarily a very small village of 300 people, there were probably more than 6,000 people in the town that night.

The shepherds then witnessed thousands of angels appearing and rejoicing and praising God. They used language the shepherds could understand to glorify God. They were especially happy that the Savior was now on earth and he would bring peace and good will to all men.

The angels did not appear to suspect that anyone on earth would refuse to accept with pleasure that God was with man, and joy and peace should reign forever. The sweetest holiest music ever heard on earth, their song, "Gloria in

Excelsis Deo," is deeply imbedded in the church and in the hearts of Christian worshipers. We venerate their choir and their music every year.

The shepherds watched the angels until they disappeared. Then they decided to go into Bethlehem and see if they could find the child as described by the heavenly beings. Their desire to find their sign was not a signal of their unbelief, but rather their desire to confirm the blessing God had given them.

They had the opportunity to see this wonderful child themselves and they were going to take advantage of it. They left their sheep, and ran down into the valley and up the hill into the town. It took them about half an hour's hard running to get there in the middle of the night. They probably ran to each place where they knew a manger was located to determine if a child had just been born there. They did not have much trouble locating the cave of the innkeeper. As townspeople. they were intimately familiar with the area. They found the child laying in the manger just as the angel had told them. They immediately fell down and worshiped their Savior.

The shepherds did not ask questions about how this child would be the Savior. They didn't discuss the theology nor the politics of the situation. They simply told everyone they could about their miraculous experience and the baby they had found just as they had been told. They believed, and their simple belief led others to begin talking about this miraculous event. The thousands who heard the story in the area could not explain what had happened. They simply talked about it and wondered what was going on.

Mary kept thinking about what had been happening to her and how everything recently associated with her had been miraculous. She could see the connection between all the events from the announcement of her pregnancy by the angel to the shepherds coming to the birth of her son in the middle of the night. She knew Jesus Christ was special. It was based upon her telling her experiences that the world would become familiar with the Christmas story.

The shepherds returned to their pastures and flocks praising God. They were joyous for two reasons, what they had heard and what they had seen. They were extremely joyous because the most important event in human history had been announced to the working men on the night shift.

Neither kings nor great men had been selected for the good news. Instead, the good news and the sign had been given to the most simple and commonest of all people. It was the shepherds who first knew that all prophesies and all anticipations were fulfilled. Is it any wonder they returned to work full of great joy? For them, and the world, it had been a night to remember always.